SHORT PLAYS FOR READING AND ACTING

Short Plays

FOR READING AND ACTING

Selected and presented by Bruce Vance

LANGUAGE STUDY CENTRE/TORONTO BOARD OF EDUCATION

Clarke, Irwin & Company Limited, Toronto, Vancouver

ISBN 0-7720-0323-8

Printed in Canada

3 4 5 6 JD 75 74 73 72

acknowledgements

The author and publishers wish to thank the publishing companies and authors listed here for permission to include the following plays: COMING THROUGH THE RYE, by William Saroyan. Copyright 1942, William Saroyan. Used with permission of the author.
PULLMAN CAR HIAWATHA, from *The Long Christmas Dinner and Other Plays*, by Thornton Wilder. Copyright 1931 by Yale University Press and Coward McCann, Inc. Copyright © 1959 by Thornton Wilder. By permission of Harper & Row, Publishers, Incorporated. Caution: *The Long Christmas Dinner and Other Plays in One Act* is the sole property of the author and is fully protected by copyright. The plays herein may not be acted by professionals or amateurs without formal permission and the payment of a royalty. All rights, including professional, amateur, stock, radio and television, broadcasting, motion picture, recitation, lecturing, public reading, and the rights of translation into foreign languages are reserved. All professional inquiries and all requests for amateur rights should be addressed to Samuel French, 25 West 45 Street, New York, 19, N.Y.
The play PROTEST, from *Worlds Apart*, by Norman Williams, is published with the permission of The Copp Clark Publishing Company. School groups wishing to perform PROTEST must secure permission from Copp Clark and pay a royalty of $5.00 for each performance.
THE RISING OF THE MOON, by Lady Gregory. Reprinted by permission of Colin Smythe Limited, publishers of *The Collected Works of Lady Gregory*.
THE PEN OF MY AUNT, by Miss Gordon Daviot. Used with permission of David Higham Associates, Ltd., Literary Executors of Miss Daviot, and of Peter Davies Ltd., Publishers of Miss Daviot's plays.

TRIFLES, by Susan Glaspell. Copyright 1951, Walter H. Baker Company. Used with permission of Walter H. Baker Company.
SORRY, WRONG NUMBER, by Lucille Fletcher. Copyright © 1948 by Lucille Fletcher. Reprinted by permission of William Morris Agency, Inc.
VISIT TO A SMALL PLANET, from *Visit to a Small Planet and Other Television Plays*, by Gore Vidal. Copyright © 1956 by Gore Vidal. By permission of Little, Brown and Company.
THE WEANS, by Robert Nathan, based on "Digging the Weans," a short story which appeared in Harper's Magazine in 1956, and was subsequently published by Alfred A. Knopf, Inc. in a book entitled *The Weans*, copyright 1956, 1959, 1960. Used with permission.
The author and publishers also gratefully acknowledge permission to quote from the following works:
A LIFE IN THE THEATRE, by Tyrone Guthrie. Copyright 1959, Tyrone Guthrie. Used with permission of McGraw-Hill Book Company.
The *Preface* to AT MY HEART'S CORE, by Robertson Davies. Copyright 1950, Clarke, Irwin & Company Limited. Used with permission of Clarke, Irwin & Company Limited.
The *Note* to THE RISING OF THE MOON, by Lady Gregory. From *The Collected Plays of Lady Gregory* which are part of *The Coole Edition* of Lady Gregory's works, published by Colin Smythe Limited. Used with permission of Colin Smythe Limited, Publishers.

contents

I believe that a theatre, where live actors perform to an audience which is there in the flesh before them, will survive all threats from powerfully organized industries which pump prefabricated drama out of cans and blowers and contraptions of one sort or another. The struggle for survival may often be hard and will batter the old theatre about severely. Indeed, from time to time it will be hardly recognizable; but it will survive. ***A Life in the Theatre*, Tyrone Guthrie**

prologue: a few words about the difference between plays acted and plays read

from the preface to *At My Heart's Core*

Robertson Davies

A playwright, of course, would always rather have the public encounter his play in the theatre than in a book. . . . The chief reason for this is that a play which acts well is written with the special capabilities and needs of actors in mind. A playwright who takes his business seriously knows that a competent actor can express with a look or gesture what might require two or three speeches to express in words. Consequently the writer tries his best to leave to his actors what they can express more economically than himself, and to put in his dialogue only what is needed to tell his story, and ornament it suitably.

Because of this special sort of economy, dramatic dialogue which reads roughly may act smoothly, for the actor knows what to do with it. And actors, it may be said, are grateful to a playwright who does not insist that they do all their work through the medium of speech, but who permits them to use their talents for gesture, bodily movement, and the conjuring up of emotion.

Competent actors, it must also be said, do not dislike long speeches; on the contrary, they like them. They bring to such speeches a vocal technique, and an understanding of phrasing and pauses, which illuminates the speech and may make it a high spot in the play. But on paper long speeches distress some readers. A play which contains them must, they believe, be "talky." They have not considered that in daily life people quite often talk for three or four minutes at a stretch without hesitation, and that, moreover, such talkers are not trained to make what they have to say pleasing to the ear. And yet these people are not usually accused of being "talky."

While on this subject it may as well be said that plays consist entirely of talk, and that there must be enough talk in an ordinary play to pass the time between half-past eight and eleven o'clock.

Comparatively few plays contain scenes in which the one-eyed Chinaman takes five minutes to murder the butler and shove him through a trapdoor in the floor—all in dumbshow. People on the stage eat, kiss, walk about, stare pensively into the fire, and so forth, but most of the time they must talk, if they expect the audience to remain in the theatre. Therefore it is not the amount of the talk, but the quality of the talk, which really counts. And however high that quality may be, gifted actors can raise it higher still.

These considerations make it hard for many people to read a play. Much of the colour which would be supplied in a novel by the descriptive passages is missing in the text of the play; it is the actor's job to supply that, with the director's aid. And many of the best moments in a stage production cannot be captured in the printed stage directions. . . . The playwright's work is completed by the actor; the reader is not often so imaginative as to be able to discover in the text of the play he is reading the qualities which would be revealed in it by a group of capable actors and an able director who had worked on it for a month.

One of the greatest advantages which a play, on the stage, enjoys over other forms of writing is that the audience experiences it as a body, and the feelings which the play arouses are communicated in some measure from one auditor to another. When others are laughing, we are more likely to laugh ourselves, and to laugh longer and louder. So also we are worked upon more strongly by scenes of tender emotion when others about us are being similarly moved.

SHORT PLAYS FOR READING AND ACTING

COMING THROUGH THE RYE WILLIAM SAROYAN

REHEARSAL

SPEECH
is the most important medium through which an actor communicates with his audience.

A skilled actor follows basic rules when he speaks on stage: *he imitates the rhythm of everyday conversation,* but he also helps his audience to understand the actions and the personality of the character he is impersonating by *stressing certain words and phrases* and *adopting a certain tone of voice.*

He is using his voice as one means of projecting across the footlights which separate the actor from his audience an impression that an imaginary person is, for the moment, real.

1/ Although an actor tries to approximate ordinary conversation, why would his speeches prove difficult for the audience to follow if he spoke, on stage, as if he were in your own living room?

2/ If, however, he were to stress certain words and phrases too strongly, what effect would this have on the audience's impression of the character he is playing?

3/ Why would his performance also likely be criticized, if, by the tone of his voice, he overemphasized a particular personality trait of the character he is portraying?

Sometimes, when he thinks it is especially important, the playwright provides *stage directions*, instructing the actors how to speak certain lines. More often, however, he depends on the actors' own abilities to interpret character, assuming that they have closely observed how people speak in different situations.

4/ Imagine that you have been assigned the role of a nine-year-old boy. At a specific point in the action of the play, you are to communicate to the audience that you are disappointed about something that was (or was not) to happen the next day. Compose a speech for the character in this situation.

a) How closely have you *imitated* the style in which a young boy would speak?

b) What words did you *emphasize* to make the boy's problem clear to the audience?

c) How have you indicated, by the *tone* of your voice, that your character is disappointed?

5/ Now suppose that you have been cast in the role of a seventy-year-old man who is looking back on a long and happy life. Invent the reply such a character might make to the seven-year-old's expression of his disappointment.

You will meet both these characters in the play which follows; you have been rehearsing by practising two of the roles. Before the class reading of the play (preferably with students taking the roles at the front of the classroom) should come *your* first reading of the play to yourself, and *your* visualizing, as clearly as you can, the other imaginary inhabitants of the dramatic world of William Saroyan's "Coming through the Rye."

Coming Through the Rye

Characters

THE VOICE

BUTCH, *a boy of nine*

MR. CARROLL, *a man of seventy*

STEVE, *about twenty-seven*

MISS QUICKLY

SEVEN KIDS: ROOSEVELT, *coloured, aged three;* ALICE, *aged five;* LARRY, *aged seven;* PEDRO GONZALEZ, *Mexican, aged eight;* JOHNNY GALLANTI, *Italian, aged nine;* BUTCH; HENRIETTA, *aged thirteen*

RALPH HASTINGS, *well-dressed, about twenty-seven*

PEGGY

Scene: A large room, beyond which is visible, in varying degrees of light and movement, infinite space, sun, moon, planets, stars, constellations, and so on.

The room is one of many. It is The American Room, and is so marked.

Each person here has been conceived and is waiting to be born. Each possesses his ultimate physical form and ego. Ultimate, that is, in the sense that here, in this waiting room, he is the way he shall be the day he begins to die, or the day he dies, in the world.

The faces of the unconceived appear to be a white cloud of a summer afternoon.

A solemn but witty VOICE *speaks.*

THE VOICE: O.K., people. Your time has come. You are now going to enter the world. You'll find it a strange place. There are no instructions. You know your destiny now, but the moment you are in the world, breathing, you shall forget it. You can thank God for that, let me tell you. Good things, and bad, are ahead for each of you. The world is still new, and the idea of sending you out there for a visit has not yet proved itself to be a good one. It may in time, though. Your destination is America. *(a phrase of patriotic music)* It's an interesting place. No better and no worse than any other place, except of course superficially, which the Americans make a good deal of, one way or the other. The climate's fair everywhere, excellent here and there. Everything you do, you shall imagine is your own doing. You can thank God for that, too. You shall live as long as you shall. No more. You will find noise and confusion everywhere, even in your sleep. Sometimes in sleep, however, you shall almost, but not quite, return to this place. Nothing in the world is important. Many things shall *seem* important. Many shall seem *unimportant.* In a moment you shall begin to be human. You have waited here nine months of the world's time. A few of you a little less. From now on you shall be alone in body, apparently cut off from everything. You shall also *seem* to be alone in spirit. That, however, is an illusion. Each of you is the continuation of two others, each of whom was a continuation of two others, each of whom— and so on. *(blithely)* I could go on talking for two or three years, but it wouldn't mean anything. O.K., now, here you go! Take a deep breath! *(dramatically)* Hold it! You will exhale in the world. O. K., Joe, let 'em out!

(A few chords of music. Some PEOPLE *go out.* BUTCH, *a boy of nine, and* MR. CARROLL, *a man of seventy, come in.* BUTCH *is thoughtfully bouncing an old tennis ball.)*

BUTCH: Well, we're next, Mr. Carroll. Do you like the idea of being born?

CARROLL: Why, yes, of course, Butch. There's nothing like getting born and being alive.

BUTCH: I don't know whether I'm lucky or unlucky. Steve says I'm lucky because I don't have to stay in the world very long, and Miss Quickly—she says it ain't fair.

CARROLL: What *ain't?*

BUTCH: Me having to get born, just for nine years. Before I get a chance to turn around I'll have to come back, so what's the use going? I'm the way I'm going to be when I die, and you're the way you're going to be when you die. I'm nine, and you're an old man.

CARROLL: Butch, my boy, those nine years are going to be wonderful.

BUTCH: Maybe. Miss Quickly says it'll take me five or six years just to begin. Gosh, that only leaves three. I won't even get a chance to see any big league baseball games.

CARROLL: Maybe you will.

BUTCH: Heck no. How am I going to get from a little town in Texas to New York?

CARROLL: It may happen.

BUTCH: Boy, I *hope* it does, but Miss Quickly—she told Steve it wasn't fair.

CARROLL: What wasn't?

BUTCH: My father dying before I'm born and my mother being poor, and dying a year later. She says I may have to go to an institution. What the heck's an institution?

CARROLL: That's an orphanage, I guess. Now, listen, Butch, don't you go worrying about anything. Everything's wonderful out there.

BUTCH: How's it really going to be?

CARROLL: Well, the minute you're out there you're alive, the same as here, only different. Out there you begin right away.

BUTCH: Begin what?

CARROLL: Living—and dying. They're both beautiful, Butch. *(happily)* Living and dying in the world. That great big little tiny place. And from the first breath you take you begin being somebody: *yourself*.

BUTCH: I'm myself right now.

CARROLL: That's because you're here waiting. You've started at last. It takes a long time to get started. It took me—well, I don't know how long exactly in the world's time—but it was a long time.

BUTCH: Steve says the world stinks.

CARROLL: Now, Steve is a young fellow with ideas. He's a nice boy, but he's wrong about the world. It's the only place for us, and any of us who get to go out there are mighty lucky.

BUTCH: What happens when we leave the world?

CARROLL: We come back.

BUTCH: Here? And wait some more?

CARROLL: Not *here*, exactly. We wait *here*, *after* we've started. When we leave the world we go back to where we were before we came here.

BUTCH: Where the heck's that?

CARROLL: It's not exactly *any* place, Butch. And it's not exactly waiting either. *This* is where we *wait*.

BUTCH: Oh, well, I guess it'll be all right. But nine years. What the heck chance will I have to see anything?

CARROLL: Butch, one day there is a long time, let alone nine years. Twenty-four hours every day. Sixty minutes every hour.

BUTCH: What are you going to be out there, Mr. Carroll?

CARROLL: *(laughing)* Oh, a lot of things, one after another.

BUTCH: Well *what?*

CARROLL: Well, let's see *(He brings out a paper and studies it.)* It says here, Thomas Carroll. Mother:

Amy Wallace Carroll. Father: Jonathan Carroll. Will be, at birth: Son, brother, nephew, cousin, grandson, and so on.

BUTCH: Brother?

CARROLL: Yes. I guess I've got a sister or a brother out there, maybe a couple of sisters and a couple of brothers.

BUTCH: I thought we were all brothers. I thought everybody was related to everybody else.

CARROLL: Oh, yes, of course, but this kind of brotherhood is closer. Whoever my brother is, he has my father and mother for *his* father and mother.

BUTCH: Well, what the heck's the difference? I thought we were all the same.

CARROLL: Oh, we are, really, but in the world there are families. They're still all really one family, but in the world the family is broken down to the people you come from, and the people that come from you. It gets pretty complicated.

BUTCH: But everybody *is* one family just the same, though, ain't they?

CARROLL: Well, yes, but in the world everybody forgets that for a while.

BUTCH: *(bringing out his paper, which is a good deal smaller than* CARROLL'S) What the heck. I never looked at this. What do I get to be? *(reading the card)* James Nelson, also called Butch. By gosh, there it is right there. Also called Butch, but my real name is James Nelson. Let's see what I get to be. *(reading)* Son. Newsboy. Schoolboy. *(reflectively)* Son. No brothers?

CARROLL: Well, I guess not, Butch.

BUTCH: Why the heck not?

CARROLL: There will be all sorts of kids out there in Texas. They'll *all* be your brothers.

BUTCH: Honest?

CARROLL: Sure.

BUTCH: *(reading)* Newsboy. What's that?

CARROLL: Well, I guess you'll sell papers.

BUTCH: Is that good?

CARROLL: Now don't you worry about anything, Butch.

BUTCH: O.K. The heck with it. *(He puts the paper away.)*

CARROLL: *(affectionately)* Give me a catch, Butch.

BUTCH: *(delighted)* No fooling?

CARROLL: Why, sure, I'm going to play second base for the New Haven Orioles.

BUTCH: *(throwing the ball, which* CARROLL *tries to catch)* Who the heck are they?

CARROLL: A bunch of kids in my neighborhood. *(He throws the ball back.)*

(STEVE *comes in. About twenty-seven, sober, serious, but a drunkard.* BUTCH *holds the ball and watches* STEVE. *Then goes to him.)*

BUTCH: Steve? Tell him about the war—and all that stuff.

STEVE: *(scarcely noticing* BUTCH, *absorbed in thought)* Tell *who, what?*

BUTCH: Mr. Carroll. About the war.

STEVE: *(looking at* CARROLL, *smiling)* I was talking to the old lady—

BUTCH: He means Miss Quickly.

STEVE: Yeah.

BUTCH: *(to* CARROLL*)* If everybody is everybody else's brother, what the heck do they have a war for?

CARROLL: Well, now, Butch—

STEVE: *(laughing solemnly)* I'm afraid you won't be able to find a good answer for that question, Doc.

BUTCH: *(delighted)* Honest, Steve?

CARROLL: Now, Steve, you know the world is a wonderful place.

STEVE: *(simply)* I'm sorry, but I think it stinks. I think the human race is unholy and disgusting. I think putting people in the world is a dirty trick.

CARROLL: No. No. No, it isn't, Steve.

STEVE: What is it, then? You're called out, everybody's a stranger, you suffer every kind of pain there is, and then you crawl back. A little tiny place that got sidetracked in space and began to fill up with terrible unclean animals in clothes.

CARROLL: Those *animals* have created several magnificent civilizations, and right now they're creating another one. It's a privilege to participate.

BUTCH: *(delighted)* You mean the World Series?
STEVE: *(wearily)* O.K., Doc. Anything you say.
CARROLL: Excuse me, Steve. Can I ask you a question?
STEVE: Anything at all.
CARROLL: What's ahead for you?
STEVE: A number of things.
CARROLL: Won't you tell me what they are?
STEVE: *(to* BUTCH*)* How about it, kid? Come back in a few minutes.
BUTCH: Ah, shucks. I want to listen. I'm not born yet.
STEVE: This is nothing. I'll be seeing you.
BUTCH: *(obedient, going to one side)* O.K., Steve.
CARROLL: What is your destiny, Steve?
STEVE: *(pause)* Murder.
CARROLL: *(amazed)* Murder?
STEVE: *(slowly)* Yes. I *am going to murder* another human being.
CARROLL: Oh, I'm sorry, Steve.
STEVE: He's here, too.
CARROLL: Here? Who is he?
STEVE: I don't know if you've noticed him. *I* have. His name is Hastings.
CARROLL: *(shocked)* Ralph Hastings?
STEVE: That's right.
CARROLL: Why, he's a nice young fellow. Are you sure it's not a mistake?
STEVE: No, it's not a mistake.
CARROLL: Well, good Lord. This is awful. But why? Why do you do it?
STEVE: It's a lot of nonsense.
CARROLL: What do you mean, Steve?
STEVE: You know he's rich. Well, he does a number of things that I think wreck the lives of poor people, so I ——If he's going to wreck the lives of people, what's he born for? If all I'm supposed to do is kill him, what am *I* born for?
CARROLL: I'm sorry, Steve. Of course you'll never know once you're out there.
STEVE: That'll help some, of course, but I just don't like the idea. What do *you* do, Doc?
CARROLL: Oh, nothing really.

STEVE: Do *you* kill anybody?
CARROLL: No, I don't, Steve. I do a lot of ordinary things.
STEVE: Do you raise a family?
CARROLL: *(delighted, but shyly)* Oh, yes. Three sons. Three daughters. All kinds of grandchildren.
STEVE: *(sincerely)* That's swell. That'll help a little.
CARROLL: Help? Help what?
STEVE: Help balance things.
CARROLL: Do *you* marry, Steve?
STEVE: Not exactly.
CARROLL: *(a little shocked but sympathetic)* Oh?
STEVE: I get a lot of women, but not a *lot* of them. I get a year of one, though. That's toward the end. She's here. *(smiling)* I'm a little ashamed of myself.
CARROLL: Why should you be ashamed?
STEVE: Well, she's Peggy.
CARROLL: *(shocked)* Peggy?
STEVE: She'll probably be all right for me by that time.
CARROLL: Peggy's really a good girl, I suppose, but she seems so——
STEVE: I don't know her very well.

*(*MISS QUICKLY *enters, with* SEVEN KIDS, *ranging in age from three to thirteen:* ROOSEVELT, *coloured, aged 3.* ALICE, *aged 5.* LARRY, *aged 7.* PEDRO GONZALEZ, *Mexican, aged 8.* JOHNNY GALLANTI, *Italian, aged 9.* BUTCH. HENRIETTA, *aged 13.)*

MISS QUICKLY: Now, children, what'll it be? Singing or play-acting?
SOME: Singing.
SOME: Play-acting.
ROOSEVELT: *(emphatically, as if with a grudge)* Nothing.
MISS QUICKLY: Nothing, Roosevelt? Now, really, you want to sing, don't you?
ROOSEVELT: No.
MISS QUICKLY: You want to act in a play, don't you?
ROOSEVELT: No.
MISS QUICKLY: You want to——
ROOSEVELT: No. I don't want to do nothing.
MISS QUICKLY: But *why*, Roosevelt?
ROOSEVELT: Because.

MISS QUICKLY: Because, what?
ROOSEVELT: Because I don't.
MISS QUICKLY: Don't you want to have fun?
ROOSEVELT: No.
MISS QUICKLY: *(patiently)* But why, child?
ROOSEVELT: Because.
MISS QUICKLY: Oh, dear.
STEVE: *(calling)* Come here Roosevelt.
ROOSEVELT: *(going to* STEVE*)* She's always making us do stuff.
MISS QUICKLY: *(gaily, to* STEVE*)* Oh, thank you, Steve. All right children, we'll sing.
ROOSEVELT: *(getting up into* STEVE's *arms)* They're going to sing! She's *always* making people sing, or something. *(looking at* MISS QUICKLY*)* Shame on you!
STEVE: You stick with me, pardner.
ROOSEVELT: Wants 'em to play-act.
MISS QUICKLY: *(sharply)* All right, children! *(she blows the pitch)* "Beautiful Dreamer" by Stephen Foster. Ready. One, two, three: Sing!

(MISS QUICKLY *and the* CHILDREN *sing the song.)*

That was fine, children. Now, Roosevelt, don't you want to sing?
ROOSEVELT: *(opening his eyes)* Shame on you—talk to me that way!
MISS QUICKLY: My gracious! Come along, children!

(They go to one side. RALPH HASTINGS *comes in, looks around. He is a well-dressed, decent sort of fellow, same age as* STEVE, *but younger looking. He looks at the coloured boy, runs his hand through the kid's hair.)*

HASTINGS: How's the boy?
ROOSEVELT: No.
HASTINGS: *(laughing)* No, what?
ROOSEVELT: No, everything.
STEVE: *(comforting him)* O.K., kid.
ROOSEVELT: *(with anger)* Only Steve's *my* pardner.
HASTINGS: Sure.
ROOSEVELT: Steve's the best man everywhere.
HASTINGS: *(smiling at* STEVE*)* Sure, he is.

CARROLL: *(studying the two young men sadly)* Well, Mr. Hastings, here we are.

HASTINGS: By the grace of God, here we wait for the first mortal breath. Are you pleased, Mr. Carroll?

CARROLL: I can't wait to begin.

HASTINGS: You, Steve?

STEVE: *(simply)* I'm here.

HASTINGS: And so am I. *(pause)* Well——

STEVE: Look. I don't know if you know, but if you do——

HASTINGS: As a matter of fact, I *do* know, but what the hell——!

STEVE: I want you to know——

HASTINGS: *(cheerfully)* It's all right.

CARROLL: *(thoughtfully)* There must be some mistake.

HASTINGS: No, there's no mistake. Everything's in order. I'm sorry, Steve. I'll have it coming to me, I suppose.

STEVE: I don't think so.

HASTINGS: These things all balance. I *must* have it coming to me.

STEVE: That's why I say the world stinks.

HASTINGS: It depends, I guess.

STEVE: *(sincerely)* Thanks. *(to* CARROLL*)* Right now he's the way he is the day he dies, and I'm the way I am that day. It's obvious it's not him, and not me, so it *must* be the world.

HASTINGS: We're not human yet.

STEVE: You mean we're not inhuman yet.

CARROLL: Now, boys.

HASTINGS: *(cheerfully)* Of course, Mr. Carroll. *(to* STEVE*)* I have a lot of fun, after a fashion, as long as it lasts. How about you?

STEVE: *(laughs, stops)* It's O.K.

*(*PEGGY *comes in, looks around, comes over to the three men. She simply stands near them.)*

You know—I like you, Peggy. Even here, you're lost.

PEGGY: Oh, it's boring—that's what burns me up. Nothing to do. No excitement. I want to get started, so I can get it over with. I want to dance——I just heard a new one——*(singing)* "I don't want to set the world on fire."

(CARROLL *and* HASTINGS *move away.)*

STEVE: Ah, now, Peggy—sure you do.

PEGGY: All I want to do is get it over with. I'm in a hurry. When do we start?

STEVE: *(He puts* ROOSEVELT *with the other two kids.)* Any time, now—any minute. They just got rid of another mob. We're next. *(pause, while he smiles at her)* Near you, Peggy, I'm in a hurry myself. *(He takes her by the shoulders.)*

PEGGY: *(shocked a little)* Here?

STEVE: What's the difference? I've waited a long time for you. *(He takes her and kisses her.)* You see, Peggy, you're no good, and I love you for it. Because I'm no good, too. I don't know why, but it's so. Now, before we know it, we'll be separated and I won't be seeing you again for a long time. Remember me, so that when we *do* meet again, you'll know who I am.

PEGGY: I've got a poor memory, but I guess I'll know you just the same.

STEVE: *(kissing her again)* You'll remember, don't worry.

(They stand, kissing.)

THE VOICE: O.K., people! Here we go again! I'm not going to go through the whole speech. You're going out whether you like it or not, so get going, and good luck to you!

(Everybody goes. Only STEVE *and* PEGGY *stand together, kissing.)*

O.K., you two—get going!

*(*PEGGY *tries to move, but* STEVE *won't let her go.)*

Come on, come on, you American lovers, get going!

*(*PEGGY *struggles.* STEVE *holds her. She falls. He holds her terribly.)*

PEGGY: *(whispering)* Let me go—please let me go!

(They struggle passionately for some time.)

THE VOICE: What's *this?* What goes on around here?

(A whistle is blown, like a police whistle, but STEVE *clings*

to PEGGY. *At last* PEGGY *breaks away from him, gets to her feet, turns and runs.* STEVE *gets up and looks around, smiling wisely. He straightens out. As he stands, a new-born babe begins to bawl, as if it were himself being born. He looks around, turns easily, and walks out.)*

STEVE: O.K. O.K. I'm going.

CURTAIN

PRODUCTION

SETTING

places the audience in a specific place at a specific time.

The chief means by which a playwright establishes the setting is the *stage set,* for which the author may provide the *set designer* with a more or less detailed description. Often hints within the text of the play itself will also furnish the set designer with ideas.

1/ What specific details has Saroyan provided for *the set designer* at the beginning of "Coming through the Rye"?

2/ What details has the playwright left to the designer's (and the audience's) *talents and imagination?*

3/ Acting as set designer for a production of "Coming through the Rye," *sketch* the set:
a) as it would appear to the audience
b) as it would appear if you were looking down onto the stage.

4/ How important a part would *carpenters* and *painters* play in executing your set design?

COSTUME

is almost as important as the set in heightening the *visual impact* of a play. Now focus your attention, as *costume designer,* on what the characters should wear.

1/ Compare the number of details Saroyan has given the *set designer* with those he has provided for the costume designer? Which of the two craftsmen faces the greater challenge?

2/ Keeping in mind the age and personality of each of these characters, design *appropriate* costumes for:

a) Butch
b) Mr. Carroll
c) Steve
d) Hastings
e) Peggy
f) Miss Quickly.

3/ Re-consider your costume designs to ensure that you have chosen *styles* and *colours* which will help to bring out the characters' *personalities,* and will also *harmonize* with one another on stage.

REVIEW

means, to the actor, the *judgment* passed by a theatre critic on the contributions of the various craftsmen and the total effect of the production. Upon what the critics write may hinge the decision about whether the producer decides to close the play after opening night or to prepare for a long run.

Critics, being human, often arrive at the theatre with their own particular *prejudices.* What sort of review of "Coming through the Rye" do you think each of the following critics would write for his paper and its readers?

1/ Critic A expects that a good play should make *a significant comment* on man, on society, or on man's place in the universe.

2/ Critic B concentrates on how *realistically* the playwright has created, and the actors have portrayed, human beings on stage.

3/ Critic C comes to the theatre to be *entertained,* preferring to see characters and actions which transport the theatre-goer from the humdrum routine of everyday life.

RESEARCH

involves delving into specific aspects of the play *to increase your appreciation* of the playwright's craft and to heighten your awareness of the problems faced by the craftsmen who are in charge of mounting the playwright's production on the stage.

One striking aspect of "Coming through the Rye" is Saroyan's use of songs.

1/ The title of the play takes us back to Robert Burns' version of a popular Scottish song; the first two verses of his poem are pertinent to the basic structure of the play:

Coming through the Rye, poor body,
Coming through the Rye,
She draiglet a' her petticoatie,
Coming through the Rye.

Gin a body meet a body
Coming through the Rye;
Gin a body kiss a body,
Need a body cry?

a) The lady in Burns' poem crosses the Scottish River Rye with some difficulty: "She draiglet a' her petticoatie"; that is, she got her petticoat all wet.

What crossing is Peggy to make in Saroyan's play, along with the others? How is the crossing made more difficult for her? for some of the other characters?

b) What parallels do you see between the actions of the speaker in the Burns' poem and of Steve in the play?

2/ Saroyan has the children sing Stephen Foster's "Beautiful Dreamer" just before they and the others about-to-be-born enter the world of humanity:

Beautiful dreamer, wake unto me,
Starlight and dew-drops are waiting for thee;
Sounds of the rude world heard in the day,
Lull'd by the moonlight have all pass'd away!
Beautiful dreamer, queen of my song,
List while I woo thee with soft melody;
Gone are the cares of life's busy throng.
Beautiful dreamer, awake unto me!
Beautiful dreamer awake unto me!

Beautiful dreamer, out on the sea
Mermaids are chanting the wild lorelie;
Over the streamlet vapours are borne,

Waiting to fade at the bright
coming morn.
Beautiful dreamer, beam in my
heart,
E'en as the morn on thee stream-
let and sea;
Then will all clouds of sorrow
depart,
Beautiful dreamer, awake unto me!
Beautiful dreamer awake unto me!

a) What various fates await the characters in Saroyan's play when they "awake" in the real world?
b) How many of them are going to face as pleasant an existence as Foster promises his love?

c) Who are going to experience the reverse of the world of "starlight and dewdrops" and "mermaids . . . chanting"?

d) Why did Saroyan choose to have Miss Quickly direct the children in singing this particular song?

3/ Saroyan has associated Peggy with a popular song of 1941. Does Peggy "want to set the world on fire"? How do you know?

READING

other plays by the same author can often clarify for you the attitude he has towards life—which may be only partially revealed in any one of his plays.

Saroyan's "My Heart's in the Highlands," "The Time of Your Life," "Love's Old Sweet Song," "The Beautiful People" and "Hello Out There" have been published in the Bantam World Drama paperback series as *The Time of Your Life and Other Plays* (NT-10).

PULLMAN CAR HIAWATHA THORNTON WILDER

REHEARSAL

STAGE PRESENCE
is ability of an experienced actor to appear *at ease* and *in character* on stage, whether or not he is taking a direct part in the action.

In fact, standing still and apparently doing nothing is almost as difficult as being the centre of the audience's attention.

1/ As a general rule an actor, unless he is facing his audience should stand with *the foot away from the audience ahead of the other.* Why?

2/ Unless they are corrected, amateur actors usually strike awkward poses when they appear before an audience for the first time. Comment on the *posture* of the actors who read the parts in "Coming through the Rye" to the class. What effect did this have on the impact the play had on the audience? Why?

3/ Beginning actors often tend to think that they are *the centre of the audience's attention* only when *they* are *speaking.* What must the actor give the impression he is doing while others are speaking? Why?

4/ Notice the difficulties the Stage Manager faces in Wilder's play. Although he is always on stage, he is more often than not a *bystander*. How could an incompetent actor playing such a role affect the audience's conception of the play?

STAGE MOVEMENT
is as vital to an actor's characterization as the way he speaks his lines. After all, we *see* as well as *hear* the characters on stage.

Thus how an actor moves about the stage, performs certain actions and makes specific gestures might make the difference between whether the person the performer is creating is believeable or not.

The action of Thornton Wilder's play takes place in a Pullman car, a railroad sleeping car which is a later variation of the coach George Pullman remodelled as a sleeper for the Chicago and Alton Railroad in 1858. Originally these cars had only upper berths, but in 1865 Pullman and his partner patented the upper and lower berth sleeping accommodation which, except for the addition of compartments, has changed little since the first Pullman, named appropriately, "The Pioneer." Wilder's Pullman is named "Hiawatha," after the sixteenth-century North American Indian statesman and warrior.

1/ In Wilder's play the characters come onto *a bare stage*, each one carrying two chairs with which he is to *manufacture* for the audience lower berths or beds in compartments into which he or she is to retire for the night.

How do you imagine each of the following, having set up his berth, would *get into it:*

a) a maiden lady
b) a middle-aged doctor
c) a stout woman of fifty
d) a young man?

2/ Each Pullman had a porter who is in charge of catering to the passenger's needs.

Imitate how an actor playing the porter's role would indicate to the audience that:

a) the train is moving
b) that it is rounding a curve?

These and other characters you are to meet as they travel, on the night of December 21, 1930, from New York to Chicago aboard Thornton Wilder's "Pullman Car Hiawatha."

Pullman Car Hiawatha

Characters

STAGE MANAGER

COMPARTMENT THREE, *an insane woman, male attendant, trained nurse*

COMPARTMENT TWO, *Philip*

COMPARTMENT ONE, *Harriet, his young wife*

LOWER ONE, *a maiden lady*

LOWER THREE, *a middle-aged doctor*

LOWER FIVE, *a stout, amiable woman of fifty*

LOWER SEVEN, *an engineer going to California*

LOWER NINE, *another engineer*

PORTER

GROVER'S CORNERS, OHIO

THE FIELD

A TRAMP

PARKERSBURG, OHIO

TWO WORKERS

A MECHANIC

TEN, ELEVEN, AND TWELVE O'CLOCK

GABRIEL AND MICHAEL, *two archangels*

Scene: At the back of the stage is a balcony or bridge or runway leading out of sight in both directions. Two flights of stairs descend from it to the stage. There is no further scenery.

At the rise of the curtain the STAGE MANAGER *is making lines with a piece of chalk on the floor of the stage by the footlights.*

THE STAGE MANAGER: This is the plan of a Pullman car. Its name is Hiawatha and on December twenty-first it is on its way from New York to Chicago. Here at your left are three compartments. Here is the aisle and five lowers. The berths are all full, uppers and lowers, but for the purposes of this play we are limiting our interest to the people in the lower berths on the further side only.

The berths are already made up. It is half-past nine. Most of the passengers are in bed behind the green curtains. They are dropping their shoes on the floor, or wrestling with their trousers, or wondering whether they dare hide their valuables in the pillow slips during the night.

All right! Come on, everybody!

(The actors enter carrying chairs. Each improvises his berth by placing two chairs facing one another in his chalk-marked space. They then sit on one chair, profile to the audience, and rest their feet on the other. This must do for lying in bed.)

(The passengers in the compartments do the same.)
(Reading from left to right we have:

COMPARTMENT THREE: *an insane woman with a male attendant and trained nurse.*

COMPARTMENT TWO: PHILIP *and*

COMPARTMENT ONE: HARRIET, *his young wife.*

LOWER ONE: *a maiden lady.*

LOWER THREE: *a middle-aged doctor.*

LOWER FIVE: *a stout, amiable woman of fifty.*

LOWER SEVEN: *an engineer going to California.*

LOWER NINE: *another engineer.)*

LOWER ONE: Porter, be sure and wake me up at quarter of six.

PORTER: Yes, ma'am.

LOWER ONE: I know I shan't sleep a wink, but I want to be told when it's quarter of six.

PORTER: Yes, ma'am.

LOWER SEVEN: *(putting his head through the curtains)* Hsst! Porter! Hsst! How the hell do you turn on this other light?

PORTER: *(fussing with it)* I'm afraid it's outa order, suh. You'll have to use the other end.

THE STAGE MANAGER: *(falsetto, substituting for some woman in an upper berth)* May I ask if someone in this car will be kind enough to lend me some aspirin?

PORTER: *(rushing about)* Yes, ma'am.

LOWER NINE: *(one of the engineers, descending the aisle and falling into Lower Five)* Sorry, lady, sorry. Made a mistake.

LOWER FIVE: *(grumbling)* Never in all my born days!

LOWER ONE: *(in a shrill whisper)* Porter! Porter!

PORTER: Yes, ma'am.

LOWER ONE: My hot-water bag's leaking. I guess you'll have to take it away. I'll have to do without it tonight. How awful!

LOWER FIVE: *(sharply to the passenger above her)* Young man, you mind your own business, or I'll report you to the conductor.

STAGE MANAGER: *(substituting for* UPPER FIVE*)* Sorry, ma'am, I didn't mean to upset you. My suspenders fell down and I was trying to catch them.

LOWER FIVE: Well, here they are. Now go to sleep. Everybody seems to be rushing into my berth tonight.

(She puts her head out.)

Porter! Porter! Be a good soul and bring me a glass of water, will you? I'm parched.

LOWER NINE: Bill!

(no answer)

Bill!

LOWER SEVEN: Ye'? Wha' d'y'a want?

LOWER NINE: Slip me one of those magazines, willya?

LOWER SEVEN: Which one d'y'a want?

LOWER NINE: Either one. *Detective Stories.* Either one.

LOWER SEVEN: Aw, Fred. I'm just in the middle of one of'm in *Detective Stories.*

LOWER NINE: That's all right. I'll take the Western. Thanks.

THE STAGE MANAGER: *(to the actors)* All right! Sh! Sh! Sh—

(to the audience)

Now I want you to hear them thinking.

(There is a pause and then they all begin a murmuring-swishing noise, very soft. In turn each one of them can be heard above the others.)

LOWER FIVE: *(the lady of fifty)* Let's see: I've got the doll for the baby. And the slip-on for Marietta. And the fountain pen for Herbert. And the subscription to *Time* for George. . . .

LOWER SEVEN: *(Bill)* God! Lillian, if you don't turn out to be what I think you are, I don't know what I'll do. I guess it's bad politics to let a woman know that you're going all the way to California to see her. I'll think up a song and dance about a business trip or something. Was I ever as hot and bothered about anyone like this before? Well, there was Martha. But that was different. I'd better try and read or I'll go cuckoo. "How did you know it was ten o'clock when the visitor left the house?" asked the detective. "Because at ten o'clock," answered the girl, "I always turn out the lights in the conservatory and in the back hall. As I was coming down the stairs I heard the master talking to someone at the front door. I heard him say, 'Well, good night. . . .' "—Gee, I don't feel like reading; I'll just think about Lillian. That yellow hair. Them eyes! . . .

LOWER THREE: *(The* DOCTOR *reads aloud to himself from a medical journal the most hair-raising material, every now and then punctuating his reading with an interrogative "So?")*

LOWER ONE: *(the maiden lady)* I know I'll be awake all night. I might just as well make up my mind to it now. I can't imagine what got hold of that hot-water bag to leak on the train of all places. Well now, I'll lie on my right side and breathe deeply and think of beautiful things, and perhaps I can doze off a bit. *(and lastly)*

LOWER NINE: *(Fred)* That was the craziest thing I ever did. It's set me back three whole years. I could have saved up thirty thousand dollars by now if I'd only stayed over here. What business had I got to fool with contracts with the goddam Soviets. Hell, I thought it would be interesting. Interesting, what the hell! It's set me back three whole years. I don't even know if the company'll take me back. I'm green, that's all. I just don't grow up.

(The STAGE MANAGER *strides toward them with lifted hand, crying "Hush," and their whispering ceases.)*

THE STAGE MANAGER: That'll do! Just one minute. Porter!

THE PORTER: *(appearing at the left)* Yessuh.

THE STAGE MANAGER: It's your turn to think.

(THE PORTER *is very embarrassed.)*

Don't you want to? You have a right to.

THE PORTER: *(torn between the desire to release his thoughts and his shyness)* Ah . . . ah . . . I'm only thinkin' about my home in Chicago and . . . and my life insurance.

THE STAGE MANAGER: That's right.

THE PORTER: . . . well, thank you . . . thank you.

(He slips away, blushing violently, in an agony of self-consciousness and pleasure.)

THE STAGE MANAGER: *(to the audience)* He's a good fellow, Harrison is. Just shy.

(to the actors again)

Now the compartments, please.
(The berths fall into shadow.)

*(*PHILIP *is standing at the door connecting his compartment with his wife's.)*

PHILIP: Are you all right, angel?

HARRIET: Yes. I don't know what was the matter with me during dinner.

PHILIP: Shall I close the door?

HARRIET: Do see whether you can't put a chair against it that will hold it half open without banging.

PHILIP: There. Good night, angel. If you can't sleep, call me, and we'll sit up and play Russian bank.

HARRIET: You're thinking of that awful time when we sat up every night for a week. . . . But at least I know I shall sleep tonight. The noise of the wheels has become sort of nice and homely. What state are we in?

PHILIP: We're tearing through Ohio. We'll be in Indiana soon.

HARRIET: I know those little towns full of horse blocks.

PHILIP: Well, we'll reach Chicago very early. I'll call you. Sleep tight.

HARRIET: Sleep tight, darling.

(He returns to his own compartment. In Compartment Three, the male attendant tips his chair back against the wall and smokes a cigar. The trained nurse knits a stocking. The insane woman leans her forehead against the windowpane; that is, stares into the audience.)

THE INSANE WOMAN: *(Her words have a dragging, complaining sound but lack any conviction.)* Don't take me there. Don't take me there.

THE FEMALE ATTENDANT: Wouldn't you like to lie down, dearie?

THE INSANE WOMAN: I want to get off the train. I want to go back to New York.

THE FEMALE ATTENDANT: Wouldn't you like me to brush your hair again? It's such a nice feeling.

THE INSANE WOMAN: *(going to the door)* I want to get off the train. I want to open the door.

THE FEMALE ATTENDANT: *(taking one of her hands)* Such a

noise! You'll wake up all the nice people. Come and I'll tell you a story about the place we're going to.

THE INSANE WOMAN: I don't want to go to that place.

THE FEMALE ATTENDANT: Oh, it's lovely! There are lawns and gardens everywhere. I never saw such a lovely place. Just lovely.

THE INSANE WOMAN: *(lies down on the bed)* Are there roses?

THE FEMALE ATTENDANT: Roses! Red, yellow, white . . . just everywhere.

THE MALE ATTENDANT: *(after a pause)* That musta been Cleveland.

THE FEMALE ATTENDANT: I had a case in Cleveland once. Diabetes.

THE MALE ATTENDANT: *(after another pause)* I wisht I had a radio here. Radios are good for *them.* I had a patient once that had to have the radio going every minute.

THE FEMALE ATTENDANT: Radios are lovely. My married niece has one. It's always going. It's wonderful.

THE INSANE WOMAN: *(half rising)* I'm not beautiful. I'm not beautiful as she was.

THE FEMALE ATTENDANT: Oh, I think you're beautiful! Beautiful. Mr. Morgan, don't you think Mrs. Churchill is beautiful?

THE MALE ATTENDANT: Oh, fine lookin'! Regular movie star, Mrs. Churchill.

(She looks inquiringly at them and subsides.)

(HARRIET groans slightly. Smothers a cough. She gropes about with her hand and finds the bell.)
(The PORTER knocks at her door.)

HARRIET: *(whispering)* Come in. First, please close the door into my husband's room. Softly. Softly.

PORTER: *(a plaintive porter)* Yes, ma'am.

HARRIET: Porter, I'm not well. I'm sick. I must see a doctor.

PORTER: Why, ma'am, they ain't no doctor . . . .

HARRIET: Yes, when I was coming out from dinner I saw a man in one of the seats on *that* side reading medical papers. Go and wake him up.

PORTER: *(flabbergasted)* Ma'am, I cain't wake anybody up.

HARRIET: Yes, you can. Porter. Porter. Now don't argue

with me. I'm very sick. It's my heart. Wake him up. Tell him it's my heart.

PORTER: Yes, ma'am.

(He goes into the aisle and starts pulling the shoulder of the man in Lower Three.)

LOWER THREE: Hello. Hello. What is it? Are we there?

(The PORTER *mumbles to him.)*

I'll be right there. Porter, is it a young woman or an old one?

PORTER: I dono, suh. I guess she's kinda old, suh, but not so very old.

LOWER THREE: Tell her I'll be there in a minute and to lie quietly.

(The PORTER *enters* HARRIET'S *compartment. She has turned her head away.)*

PORTER: He'll be here in a minute, ma'am. He says you lie quiet.

(LOWER THREE: *stumbles along the aisle muttering.)*

LOWER THREE: Damn these shoes!

SOMEONE'S VOICE: Can't we have a little quiet in this car, please?

LOWER NINE: Oh, shut up!

(The DOCTOR *passes the* PORTER *and enters* HARRIET'S *compartment. He leans over her, concealing her by his stooping figure.)*

LOWER THREE: She's dead, porter. Is there anyone on the train traveling with her?

PORTER: Yessuh. Dat's her husband in dere.

LOWER THREE: Idiot! Why didn't you call him? I'll go in and speak to him.

(The STAGE MANAGER *comes forward.)*

THE STAGE MANAGER: All right. So much for the inside of the car. That'll be enough of that for the present. Now for its position geographically, meteorologically, astronomically, theologically considered.

Pullman Car Hiawatha, ten minutes of ten. December twenty-first, 1930. All ready.

(Some figures begin to appear on the balcony.)

No, no. It's not time for the planets yet. Nor the hours.
(They retire.)

(The STAGE MANAGER *claps his hands. A grinning boy in overalls enters from the left side behind the berths.)*

GROVER'S CORNER'S OHIO: *(in a foolish voice as though he were reciting a piece at a Sunday School entertainment)* I represent Grover's Corners, Ohio—821 souls. "There's so much good in the worst of us and so much bad in the best of us, that it ill behooves any of us to criticize the rest of us." Robert Louis Stevenson. Thankya.
(He grins and goes out right.)
(Enter from the same direction somebody in shirt sleeves. This is a field.)

THE FIELD: I represent a field you are passing between Grover's Corners, Ohio, and Parkersburg, Ohio. In this field there are fifty-one gophers, 206 field mice, six snakes and millions of bugs, insects, ants, and spiders, all in their winter sleep. "What is so rare as a day in June? Then, if ever, come perfect days." *The Vision of Sir Launfal,* William Cullen—I mean James Russell Lowell. Thank you. *(exit)*

(enter a tramp)

THE TRAMP: I just want to tell you that I'm a tramp that's been traveling under this car Hiawatha, so I have a right to be in this play. I'm going from Rochester, New York, to Joliet, Illinois. It takes a lotta people to make a world.

On the road to Mandalay
Where the flying fishes play
And the sun comes up like thunder
Over China cross the bay.

Frank W. Service. It's bitter cold. Thank you.
(exit)

(enter a gentle old farmer's wife with three stringy young people)

PARKERSBURG, OHIO: I represent Parkersburg, Ohio—2604

souls. I have seen all the dreadful havoc that alcohol has done, and I hope no one here will ever touch a drop of the curse of this beautiful country.

(She beats a measure and they all sing unsteadily.)

"Throw out the life line! Throw out the life line! Someone is sinking today-ay. . . ."

(The STAGE MANAGER *moves them away tactfully.)*

(enter a workman)

THE WORKMAN: Ich bin der Arbeiter der hier sein Leben verlor. Bei der Sprengung für diese Brücke über die Sie in dem Moment fahren—

(The engine whistles for a trestle crossing.)

—erschlug mich ein Felsbock. Ich spiele jetzt als Geist in diesem Stuck mit. "Vor sieben und achtzig Jahren haben unsere Väter auf diesem Continent eine neue Nation hervorgebracht. . . ."

THE STAGE MANAGER: *(helpfully, to the audience)* I'm sorry; that's in German. He says that he's the ghost of a workman who was killed while they were building the trestle over which the car Hiawatha is now passing—

(The engine whistles again.)

—and he wants to appear in this play. A chunk of rock hit him while they were dynamiting. His motto you know: "Four score and seven years ago our fathers brought forth upon this continent a new nation dedicated," and so on. Thank you, Mr. Krüger.

(exit the ghost)

(enter another worker)

THIS WORKER: I'm a watchman in a tower near Parkersburg, Ohio. I just want to tell you that I'm not asleep and that the signals are all right for this train. I hope you all have a fine trip. "If you can keep your heads when all about you are losing theirs and blaming it on you. . . ."Rudyard Kipling. Thank you. *(exit)*

(The STAGE MANAGER *comes forward.)*

THE STAGE MANAGER: All right. That'll be enough of that. Now the weather.

(enter a mechanic)

A MECHANIC: It is eleven degrees above zero. The wind is

north-northwest, velocity, 57. There is a field of low barometric pressure moving eastward from Saskatchewan to the eastern coast. Tomorrow it will be cold with some snow in the Middle Western States and northern New York. *(exits)*

THE STAGE MANAGER: All right. Now for the hours.
(helpfully to the audience)
The minutes are gossip; the hours are philosophers; the years are theologians. The hours are philosophers with the exception of Twelve O'clock who is also a theologian. Ready, Ten O'clock!

(The hours are beautiful girls dressed like Elihu Vedder's Pleiades. Each carries a great gold Roman numeral. They pass slowly across the balcony at the back, moving from right to left.)
What are you doing, Ten O'clock? Aristotle?

TEN O'CLOCK: No, Plato, Mr. Washburn.

THE STAGE MANAGER: Good. "Are you not rather convinced that he who thus. . . ."

TEN O'CLOCK: "Are you not rather convinced that he who sees beauty as only it can be seen will be specially favoured? And since he is in contact not with images but with realities. . . ."
(She continues the passage in a murmur as ELEVEN O'CLOCK *appears.)*

ELEVEN O'CLOCK: "What else can I, Epictetus, do, a lame old man, but sing hymns to God? If then I were a nightingale, I would do the nightingale's part. If I were a swan, I would do a swan's. But now I am a rational creature. . . ."
(Her voice too subsides to a murmur. TWELVE O'CLOCK *appears.)*

THE STAGE MANAGER: Good. Twelve O'clock, what have you?

TWELVE O'CLOCK: Saint Augustine and his mother.

THE STAGE MANAGER: So. "And we began to say: If to any the tumult of the flesh were hushed. . . ."

TWELVE O'CLOCK: "And we began to say: If to any the tumult of the flesh were hushed; hushed the images of earth; of waters and of air; . . ."

THE STAGE MANAGER: Faster. "Hushed also the poles of heaven."

TWELVE O'CLOCK: "Yea, were the very soul to be hushed to herself."

STAGE MANAGER: A little louder, Miss Foster.

TWELVE O'CLOCK: *(a little louder)* "Hushed all dreams and imaginary revelations. . . ."

THE STAGE MANAGER: *(waving them back)* All right. All right. Now the planets. December twenty-first, 1930, please.

(The hours unwind and return to their dressing rooms at the right. The planets appear on the balcony. Some of them take their place halfway on the steps. These have no words, but each has a sound. One has a pulsating, zinging sound. Another has a thrum. One whistles ascending and descending scales. Saturn does a slow obstinate: Mmm on notes sol-la, sol-la, etc. below middle C.)

Louder, Saturn—Venus, higher. Good. Now, Jupiter. Now the Earth.

(He turns to the beds on the train.)

Come, everybody. This is the Earth's sound.

(The towns, workmen, etc., appear at the edge of the stage. The passengers begin their "thinking" murmur.)

Come, Grover's Corners. Parkersburg. You're in this. Watchman. Tramp. This is the Earth's sound.

(He conducts it as the director of an orchestra would. Each of the towns and workmen does his motto.)

*(*THE INSANE WOMAN *breaks into passionate weeping. She rises and stretches out her arms to the* STAGE MANAGER.*)*

THE INSANE WOMAN: Use me. Give me something to do.

(He goes to her quickly, whispers something in her ear, and leads her back to her guardians. She is unconsoled.)

THE STAGE MANAGER: Now sh-sh-sh! Enter the archangels. *(to the audience)* We have now reached the theological position of Pullman car Hiawatha.

(The towns and workmen have disappeared. The

planets, off stage, continue a faint music. Two young men in blue serge suits enter along the balcony and descend the stairs at the right. As they pass each bed the passenger talks in his sleep. GABRIEL *points out* BILL *to* MICHAEL *who smiles with raised eyebrows. They pause before* LOWER FIVE, *and* MICHAEL *makes the sound of assent that can only be rendered "HnHn." The remarks that the characters make in their sleep are not all intelligible, being lost in the sound of sigh or groan or whisper by which they are conveyed. But we seem to hear:)*

LOWER NINE: *(loud)* Some people are slower than others, that's all.

LOWER SEVEN: It's no fun, y'know. I'll try.

LOWER FIVE: *(the lady of the Christmas presents, rapidly)* You know best, of course. I'm ready whenever you are. One year's like another.

LOWER ONE: I can teach sewing. I can sew.

(They approach HARRIET'S *compartment.)*

(THE INSANE WOMAN *sits up and speaks to them.)*

THE INSANE WOMAN: Me?

*(*THE ARCHANGELS *shake their heads.)*

THE INSANE WOMAN: What possible use can there be in my simply waiting? Well, I'm grateful for anything. I'm grateful for being so much better than I was. The old story, the terrible story, doesn't haunt me as it used to. A great load seems to have been taken off my mind. But no one understands me any more. At last I understand myself perfectly, but no one else understands a thing I say. So I must wait?

*(*THE ARCHANGELS *nod, smiling.)*

THE INSANE WOMAN: *(resignedly, and with a smile that implies their complicity)* Well, you know best. I'll do whatever is best; but everyone is so childish, so absurd. They have no logic. These people are all so mad. . . . These people are like children; they have never suffered.

(She returns to her bed and sleeps. The ARCHANGELS *stand beside* HARRIET. *The doctor has drawn* PHILIP *into the next compartment and is talking to him in earnest whispers.)*

(HARRIET'S *face has been toward the wall; she turns it slightly and speaks toward the ceiling.)*

HARRIET: I wouldn't be happy there. Let me stay dead down here. I belong here. I shall be perfectly happy to roam about my house and be near Philip. You know I wouldn't be happy there.

(GABRIEL *leans over and whispers into her ear. After a short pause she bursts into fierce tears.)*

I'm ashamed to come with you. I haven't done anything. I haven't done anything with my life. Worse than that: I was angry and sullen. I never realized anything. I don't dare go a step in such a place.

(They whisper to her again.)

But it's not possible to forgive such things. I don't want to be forgiven so easily. I want to be punished for it all. I won't stir until I've been punished a long long time. I want to be freed of all that—by punishment. I want to be all new.

(They whisper to her. She puts her feet slowly on the ground.)

But no one else could be punished for me. I'm willing to face it all myself. I don't ask anyone to be punished for me.

(They whisper to her again. She sits long and brokenly looking at her shoes and thinking it over.)

It wasn't fair. I'd have been willing to suffer for it myself, if I could have endured such a mountain.

(She smiles.)

Oh, I'm ashamed! I'm just a stupid and you know it. I'm just another American. But then what wonderful things must be beginning now. You really want me? You really want me?

(They start leading her down the aisle of the car.)

Let's take the whole train. There are some lovely faces on this train. Can't we all come? You'll never find anyone better than Philip. Please, please, let's all go.

(They reach the steps. The ARCHANGELS *interlock their arms as a support for her as she leans heavily on them, taking the steps slowly. Her words are half singing and half babbling.)*

But look at how tremendously high and far it is. I've

a weak heart. I'm not supposed to climb stairs. "I do not ask to see the distant scene; one step enough for me." It's like Switzerland. My tongue keeps saying things. I can't control it. Do let me stop a minute: I want to say good-bye.

(She turns in their arms.)

Just a minute, I want to cry on your shoulder.

(She leans her forehead against GABRIEL'S *shoulder and laughs long and softly.)*

Good-bye, Philip. I begged him not to marry me, but he would. He believed in me just as you do. Good-bye, 1312 Ridgewood Avenue, Oakesbury, Illinois. I hope I remember all its steps and doors and wall-papers forever. Good-bye, Emerson Grammar School on the corner of Forbush Avenue and Wherry Street. Good-bye Miss Walker and Miss Cramer who taught me English and Miss Matthewson who taught me biology. Good-bye, First Congregational Church on the corner of Meyerson Avenue and Sixth Street and Dr. McReady and Mrs. McReady and Julia. Good-bye, Papa and Mama. . . .

(She turns.)

Now I'm tired of saying good-bye. I never used to talk like this. I was so homely I never used to have the courage to talk. Until Philip came. I see now. I see now. I understand everything now.

(The STAGE MANAGER: *(to the actors)* All right. All right. Now we'll have the whole world together, please. The whole solar system, please.

(The complete cast begins to appear at the edges of the stage. He claps his hands.)

The whole solar system, please. Where's the tramp? Where's the moon?

(He gives two raps on the floor, like the conductor of an orchestra attracting the attention of his forces, and slowly lifts his hand. The human beings murmur their thoughts; the hours discourse; the planets chant or hum. HARRIET'S *voice finally rises above them all saying:)*

HARRIET: "I was not ever thus, nor asked that Thou
Shouldst lead me on . . . and spite of fears,

Pride ruled my will: remember not past years."
(The STAGE MANAGER *waves them away.)*

THE STAGE MANAGER: Very good. Now clear the stage, please. Now we're at Englewood Station, South Chicago. See the University's towers over there! The best of them all.

LOWER ONE: *(the spinster)* Porter, you promised to wake me up at quarter of six.

PORTER: Sorry, ma'am, but it's been an awful night on this car. A lady's been terrible sick.

LOWER ONE: Oh! Is she better?

PORTER: No'm. She ain't one jot better.

LOWER FIVE: Young man, take your foot out of my face.

THE STAGE MANAGER: *(again substituting for* UPPER FIVE*)* Sorry, lady, I slipped—

LOWER FIVE: *(grumbling not unamiably)* I declare, this trip's been one long series of insults.

THE STAGE MANAGER: Just one minute, ma'am, and I'll be down and out of your way.

LOWER FIVE: Haven't you got anybody to darn your socks for you? You ought to be ashamed to go about that way.

THE STAGE MANAGER: Sorry, lady.

LOWER FIVE: You're too stuck up to get married. That's the trouble with you.

LOWER NINE: Bill! Bill!

LOWER SEVEN: Ye? Wha' d'y'a want?

LOWER NINE: Bill, how much d'y'a give the porter on a train like this? I've been outa the country so long. . . .

LOWER SEVEN: Hell, Fred, I don't know myself.

THE PORTER: CHICAGO, CHICAGO. All out. This train don't go no further.
(The passengers jostle their way out and an army of old women with mops and pails enters and prepares to clean up the car.)

CURTAIN

PRODUCTION

CASTING an actor for any role is key to the success of any production.

Age, physical appearance, voice and skill in executing certain mannerisms must all be taken into consideration by the director when he selects his cast.

Keeping these considerations in mind, cast a movie or television star in each of the following roles and briefly explain why you chose that particular actor or actress for the part:

1. The Stage Manager
2. The Insane Woman
3. Philip
4. Harriet
5. The maiden lady
6. The stout woman of fifty.

REVIEW

Read the following passage from reviews of "Pullman Car Hiawatha" and comment on their accuracy, from your own point of view.

These two reviews appeared after the *publication* of *The Long Christmas Dinner and Other One Act Plays*, one of which was "Pullman Car Hiawatha."

1/ Robert Littell, writing in *The Saturday Review* of December 12, 1931:

Though the play that gives its title to the book has been produced, . . . these one-act plays seem better designed for reading than for the stage. . . .

"Pullman Car Hiawatha" is a pale, fantastic, . . . self-indulgent medley of celestial music, archangels, and lower berths that gets a little tipsy on its own fantasy. In it, Mr. Wilder enjoys himself hugely and leaves the reader with some right to wonder what it is all about."

2/ An anonymous reviewer, writing in *The Times Literary Supplement*, of December 10, 1931:

It is instructive to turn from this solid writing (plays by an Edward Garnett whom scarcely anyone remembers) to Mr. Wilder's ingenuities. . . . Mr. Wilder leaves the impression of being more interested in experimental forms than in the substance of his dramas, with the consequence that, in his hand, experiment . . . wears often . . . an air of being indulged in for its own sake.

The next three reviews were written after the play was revived, more than thirty years after its publication, opening on December 3, 1962, at the Circle in the Square Theatre in New York City.

3/ "Kenn," writing in the December 12, 1962 issue of *Variety*:

"Pullman Car Hiawatha" . . . deals with a large number of characters, some of whom are cranky or eccentric but all of whom testify to the basic goodness and worth of mankind. . . . Because the play is short, the characters are not developed, and some of Wilder's symbolism is ineffective. But the playwright's warmth, humour and love of humanity permeate the drama, and make it both touching and entertaining.

4/ Howard Taubman, in *The New York Times* of December 4, 1962:

"The occupants [of the Pullman] speak and think out loud but, apart from the girl who dies, . . . they are the thinnest hints for characters."

5/ Edith Oliver, in *The New Yorker* of December 15, 1962:

". . . Sketchy and awkward it may be, but not wispy."

RESEARCH

The narrator figure is almost as old as drama itself.

1/ Read one of the following ancient Greek plays (in translation) noting the prominence of the Chorus figures; all these are available in Penguin paperback editions.
a) *The Theban Plays,* Sophocles (L3)
b) *Alcestis and Other Plays,* Euripides (L31)
c) *The Oresteian Trilogy,* Aeschylus (L67)
What *similarities* do you find in the role the Chorus plays in a Greek play and that of the Stage Manager in "Pullman Car Hiawatha"?

2/ Wilder himself used the stage manager figure more than once in his plays: in "The Happy Journey to Trenton and Camden" which appeared in the same volume in which "Pullman Car Hiawatha" was published, and later in *Our Town,* generally regarded as the author's best play. Read one of these other plays and compare *the personality* and *the function* of the stage manager with the one in "Pullman Car Hiawatha."

3/ When "Pullman Car Hiawatha" was revived in 1962, it was played on a double bill with the Welsh playwright, Dylan Thomas' "Under Milk Wood," in which Thomas employs *two* narrators. "Under Milk Wood" has been published in paperback by New Directions (NDP 73).

Compare the narrators' roles in the two plays.

4/ What *similarities* are there between Saroyan's "Coming through the Rye" and Wilder's "Pullman Car Hiawatha"? Consider the settings; the Voice and the Stage Manager; the basic purpose of the characters' journeys; and the playwrights' comments on the American scene.

READING

The Long Christmas Dinner and Other One Act Plays includes, besides the title play, "The Happy Journey," "Pullman Car Hiawatha," "The Queens of France" and "Love and How to Cure It." The anthology is available in paperback, with an introduction by the American drama critic John Gassner, in Harper and Row Colophon Books (CN 141).

Three Plays by Thornton Wilder is composed of the author's three most famous *full-length* plays: *The Skin of Our Teeth, Our Town* and *The Matchmaker* (a Bantam paperback (ST7).

The Matchmaker inspired the hit Broadway musical, *Hello, Dolly!* (a Signet paperback T3651).

THE SHIP OF DREAMS JOHN HUGHES

REHEARSAL

GESTURES
by themselves can often communicate certain elements of a character's personality even before the actor utters a word on stage and can certainly consolidate the impression a character makes on the audience.

1/ You have been cast in the role of *a middle-aged woman* "who is inclined towards *nervous movements* and is *rarely still* for a moment."

What gestures would help you to emphasize her character? When we first meet her she is setting the table for breakfast. What should she do to indicate that she feels *insecure,* and is, according to her husband, *inefficient?*

2/ Her husband feels that the whole world is against him and he takes out his ill-temper on almost everything and everyone about him.

On his first appearance we see him checking the account books of his small business.

What gestures would a skilled actor employ to show that he feels he is *losing* his battle with the world around him?

3/ The couple's only child, their son, has just quit school but he is not very interested in working in his father's grocery store.

How would you, in this role, employ certain gestures to suggest that the young man, as he comes down for breakfast, is restless, unhappy and reluctant to face another day in the store?

FACIAL EXPRESSION

a more subtle technique than gesture, is also useful in communicating character and mood; the actor skilled in revealing emotion and personality by this means more thoroughly convinces his audience of the reality of the character he is portraying.

1/ The mother we described in question 1 has a tendency to "dreaminess."

How, by *facial expression*, could an actress prepare the audience for the later revelation in dialogue of this characteristic?

2/ The father regards his son with scorn.

What facial expression would an actor employ in order to show the actor's contempt for his son when they meet at breakfast?

Such a father, mother, and son you meet in
John Hughes'
"Ship of Dreams."

The Ship of Dreams

Characters

AGNES DALEY

THOMAS DALEY

TOM DALEY

MRS. SMALL

DANNY

JEAN

A SAILOR

Scene: The general store and living-room of the Daley home, Cardiff Docks, Wales.
Time: The present. Early morning.

The scene is the Daley home and shop, in the docklands of Cardiff, Wales.

The stage is divided into two sections. One half represents the living room. It is bright and comfortable, though not luxurious: there even may be an impression of rather meagre resources made the most of by careful husbandry. There is a doorway to the kitchen; another to the upstairs portion of the house. A third door leads to the small general store, which is cluttered with an assortment of everything village housewives might need. A door leads from the shop into the street. A large window offers a panoramic view of the district.

In the living-room, AGNES DALEY *is laying the breakfast table. She is a small, faded woman in her forties. She is inclined toward nervous movements and is rarely still for a moment. Her dress is neat but plain, verging on dowdiness. She is a gentle, harmless creature tending toward dreaminess and inefficiency. She casts an anxious glance toward the shop where* THOMAS DALEY *is muttering and scowling over notebooks and ledgers, which contain the mathematical details of his struggle with the universe.* AGNES *turns to the upstairs door and softly calls:*

AGNES: Tom! Tom!

TOM: *(offstage)* Coming, ma'm.

(A moment later, TOM DALEY, *sixteen, enters. There is a resemblance between mother and son: both are fair and fine-boned. He also has inherited something of* AGNES' *dreaminess.)*

TOM: Morning, ma'm.

AGNES: My, but you're late this morning. And in your first week full-time in the shop, too! You'd best hurry now. *(She settles him at the table; watches him affectionately as he starts his morning meal.)* You look a bit pale. Feel all right, son?

TOM: Yes.

AGNES: Sure?

TOM: *(with mild impatience, for this fussing is a permanent tendency with* AGNES*)* I'm all right, ma'm. Just up reading late, that's all.

AGNES: Well, you don't want to overdo it, Tom. It's not good for you, all this reading late at night. And you know how your father feels about it. *(pause)* What was the book?

TOM: *The Nigger of the Narcissus. (pause)*

AGNES: I don't know if you ought to be reading that sort of stuff, dear.

TOM: That sort of stuff?

AGNES: Now, you know what I mean!

TOM: *(smiling)* Ma'm, you're the limit! It's not that sort of book at all. It's about the sea. By a man named Conrad. And as I read it in no time at all, I'm away to those places he describes. The real life! Away from Tiger Bay and the shop and everything; all this dull pattern of day after day the same—nothing happening. *This* is the part that isn't real. *(He hesitates; glances up at her.)* Sounds daft, does it?

AGNES: *(softly)* When I was a girl I was something of a reader too. I know what you mean, lad. Now I never seem to be able to sit down for a read like I used to.

TOM: Maybe you'd be able to, if he wasn't always—

AGNES: *(gently)* Now, never mind all that! Get on with your breakfast, that's real enough! And do hurry, son, your father's not in a very good mood this morning.

TOM: Has the post come yet?

AGNES: There was a card for you.

TOM: *(about to rise)* Where?

AGNES: Keep your seat, lad. I'll fetch it! *(She crosses to the mantelpiece and returns with a picture postcard, reading slowly.)* Fujiyama. Now where's that? China?

TOM: Jock Dean went to Yokohama this trip. Said that he would send a card! *(takes card from* AGNES *and eagerly reads it)* He writes that he'll bring me back a geisha!

AGNES: Whatever that might be, I don't know how you'd find space for it in your room! It's cluttered up to the ceiling very near already with your bits and pieces!

TOM: *(smiling)* Oh, I'd find room all right!

AGNES: How big is it, anyhow?

TOM: *(gesturing)* Oh, about so high and weighs a hundred pounds, maybe.

AGNES: A hundred pounds? What on earth is it?

TOM: A song-and-dance girl.

AGNES: *(rumpling his hair; affectionately)* I'll song-and-dance you! I wouldn't put it past that Jock Dean either!

TOM: This is the only card I've got of Fujiyama. Probably came in on that Japanese ship yesterday. It's down at the docks.

AGNES: *(urgently)* Be as quick with your breakfast as you can, Tom! He really is in a bad mood today, and it's best not to aggravate him.

TOM: *(distantly)* Just think, ma'm, for the last month or so, while we've been stuck here, she's been making her way from, maybe Nagasaki, through the China Sea to Singapore, up the Malay Straits to Colombo, through the Red Sea to Suez, and the Med, across the Bay of Biscay to here. Or maybe she sailed east to Panama, through the—

AGNES: *(interrupting his reverie)* In any case, I don't suppose it matters much. Want some more tea?

TOM: *(nods)* You don't much like the sea, do you, ma'm?

AGNES: *(pouring)* That trip I took to Ilfracombe with your father was enough for me!

TOM: Aw, ma'm, a trip across the Channel to Ilfracombe isn't a true voyage.

AGNES: Maybe not. But it's the best imitation that I want to see!

TOM: And that was years ago.

AGNES: *(reflectively)* Yes, it would be just about twenty. The summer the war broke out, it was. *(Her thoughts go back to other times, as she slowly repeats:)* Twenty years. *(With a sudden jolt, she returns to the present.)* And I *still* feel sick when I think about it! *(again wistfully)* But sometimes I think it would be nice to travel across the sea to visit Belle.

TOM: Auntie Belle? In Montreal?

AGNES: *(tidying up)* You don't remember her, do you?

TOM: She went over in 'forty-seven. I'd be only three years old.

AGNES: She had long, bright golden hair. It seemed to fascinate you, Tom. Whenever she came into the room, you used to reach out for it until she took you up and then you would cling to the strands—

TOM: *(embarrassed)* Aw, ma'm, cut it out! You're putting me off my breakfast!

AGNES: It would be nice to take a trip to Montreal.

TOM: Then why haven't you gone?

AGNES: And what would we use for fare? Old tea packets?

TOM: Tea packets! Reminds me of old Tommy Lipton in there! *(He indicates the shop with his head.)*

AGNES: *(firmly)* Now, Tom, I won't have you speaking of him like that. He's your father.

TOM: So he keeps telling me.

AGNES: Tom!

TOM: You know he could afford to take you over for a holiday if he wanted to!

AGNES: I don't know any such thing! You've got the wrong idea of the money he's supposed to possess.

TOM: I've got a better idea than he thinks of how much money passes over that shop counter! *(pause)* Aw, never mind about him, ma'm. One day, I'll have the money to take you over myself.

AGNES: Oh, you will, will you, young man?

TOM: I will that! And we'll take Auntie Alice along an' all.

AGNES: For sure, we wouldn't have to ask her twice! She'd be game for anything. They were a right pair together, her and Belle. *(businesslike)* And where would you be getting the money for our air passages, may I ask?

TOM: *(horrified) Air passages?!* Who's mentioned air passages? And miss that first sight of the New World? The same view that Cartier saw—and the millions of others who've since followed him? Miss seeing the St. Lawrence and the Citadel of Quebec and Montreal slowly coming into sight? By sea, ma'm, is the *only* way!

AGNES: All very romantic, I dare say, but there's nothing very romantic about the way my stomach behaves on a sea voyage! No, young man, if you're going to treat us to a trip, then it's by air, or not at all!

TOM: *(soberly)* Shortly, I'll leave, ma'm, and make the money, so's we could take that trip, by air then, if you'd like. *(The smile leaves* AGNES' *face.)* What's the matter, ma'm?

AGNES: *(heavily)* Lately you seem to talk of nothing else but leaving.

TOM: Would you like to see me in this shop all my life, with him?

AGNES: *(shakes her head)* Just that I can't imagine the place without you, lad. If it weren't for you being here, I don't think I could—

TOM: Why don't *you* up and go, too?

AGNES: Tom!

TOM: You could move in with Auntie Alice. Since Uncle Harry died she's been alone in that house. She'd be glad to have you come.

AGNES: *(firmly, because the thought has been in her mind often enough, despite her attempts to shut it out)* Tom, that's enough! I don't want to hear you say that again! *(pause.* TOM *sits slumped at the table, despondently. She goes to him; tenderly.)* Another tea, lad?

TOM: Please.

AGNES: I thought that would tempt you, you old boozer!

(They smile uneasily at each other as though they were trying to eliminate from their minds the last exchanges of conversation. There is a bellow from the shop, as AGNES *pours another cup of tea for* TOM. DALEY *is fuming as he goes over his books and ledgers. Now the lights come up on the shop and we see him clearly for the first time. He is a short, paunchy man with a large bald head with a few strands of black hair carefully brushed across to give maximum coverage to his white and shining pate. He sports a small moustache which does nothing to achieve the desired effect of adding strength to his weak and petulant face. He wears a thick silver watch chain over his paunch; attached to the chain is a large, old-fashioned turnip watch, a legacy from his father. His voice is loud—unctuous when addressing customers and equals, but with a mean edge when addressing his family, particularly* TOM. *With* AGNES, *too, he tries to infuse his impressions of the tones of a lord and master.)*

DALEY: *(shouting)* Agnes! Come here a minute!

(At the sound of his voice, TOM *automatically tenses up. The lights dim in the living-room.* AGNES *flutters nervously into the shop.* DALEY *has seated himself in his chair behind the desk, preparatory to enjoying the familiar scene ahead.)*

AGNES: Yes, dear? What's wrong?

DALEY: Suppose *you* tell *me!*

AGNES: *(timidly:)* The till totals again?

DALEY: Aye, the till totals! *(He pauses ominously.)* Yesterday, you will be delighted to hear, we were three and six short!

AGNES: Oh?

DALEY: Aye, oh! That amounts to over a pound a week and over fifty pounds a year. Fifty pounds! Now, what do you say?

AGNES: I dare say that you're right, dear—

DALEY: *(interposing)* I *know* I'm right!

AGNES: —but don't you think it is a bit silly to think of it like that?

DALEY: *(angrily; he resents being thought ridiculous)* Silly? Silly?! I don't suppose it matters about our profits trickling away?

AGNES: It doesn't happen very often, dear, at least—

DALEY: *Too* often! Never a week goes by without some mistake. I keep telling you that it's got to stop! Aye, it isn't all your fault! Is he up out of his weary bed, yet?

AGNES: Yes. He's almost finished his breakfast.

DALEY: Hmm, I suppose that's something to be grateful for! He knows where half the blame for those mistakes lie, all right! If they *are* mistakes, that is.

AGNES: Thomas! How can you talk about the boy like that?

DALEY: *(pause)* Maybe you're right: he wouldn't have the gumption!

(He rises, crosses to centre of the shop; shouts to TOM, *who has been sitting hunched tensely at the table.)*

Tom! Are you going to lounge in there all day?

(TOM *drains his cup; rises, sullenly.)*

Tom!

TOM: Coming, Dad.

(TOM *moves to the door, as* AGNES *returns to the living-room. They exchange swift commiserative glances as they pass each other.* TOM *enters the shop; as he does, he seems to withdraw into himself, giving an appearance of slow-wittedness, even stupidity. He has found this his best defence. Some of his remarks have an ironic twist and* DALEY *is not quite sure how* TOM *intends them, but he prefers to take them as fresh evidence of the boy's stupidity.* AGNES *busies herself between the living-room and offstage kitchen.)*

DALEY: It doesn't seem to matter to you how late you stroll in, does it?

TOM: It's only ten past nine—

DALEY: Haven't I told you a thousand times: attention to details gets the results?

TOM: *(retiring completely into his shell)* Yes, Dad. Sorry.

DALEY: *(sneering at this supposed lack of spirit) Sorry!* Do you suppose Tom Lipton was the sort of man to creep around being sorry?

TOM: Sorry for what?

DALEY: Sorry for what! Sometimes, I think I'm confronting an idiot! Wouldn't surprise me if you didn't know *who* Tom Lipton was!

TOM: I hear about him every day.

DALEY: Then learn something from him, can't you? Do you suppose Tom Lipton came strolling into the shop when the day was half done and over?

TOM: No.

DALEY: He was there at the shop before the world was awake and he was still there when it went to bed! *(sharply)* Don't stand there doing nothing! Give those cans a wipe, can't you? Waste not the idle moment! *(He resumes his pontification.)* Tom Lipton! A name and a man to remember—and learn from. Energy, vision, and attention to detail—years and years of it —and where did he end up?

TOM: *(lethargically, dusting tins)* He's dead, Dad.

DALEY: I *know* he's dead, you fool, but where was he *before* he died? *(*TOM *shakes his head mutely.* DALEY *leans over, and with heavy emphasis, declares:)* On top, that's where he was! Right at the top! All through metic—metic—*(He is stuck with the word.)*

TOM: Do you mean meticulous?

DALEY: *(He resents being corrected by his son.)* Yes, I do mean metic-ul-ous! His attention to detail got him to the top. Attention to detail and energy! *(He emphasizes the latter by tapping with his pencil on the ledger. The lesson for the morning over, he glances at his watch.)* Well, can I rely on you to take over while I grab some breakfast?

TOM: Yes, Dad.

(There is a ping of the shop bell and MRS. SMALL *enters. She is a typical housewife of the district, dressed for early morning marketing. She wears slippers; her bare legs reveal fire scorch marks. A dust-cap with a few protruding hair curlers crowns her time-worn head.* DALEY *immediately switches to his professional smile.)*

DALEY: Morning, Mrs. Small. And what's your pleasure?

MRS. SMALL: Morning, Mr. Daley. I'll just 'ave some instant coffee, a tin of 'am, and a couple of tins o' peas. I think that's about all.

DALEY: *(receiving the order with a bland smile)* Certainly, Mrs. Small. *(The smile vanishes, as he turns to* TOM.*)* Tom! Fetch Mrs. Small's order. And don't short-change her! *(Both he and* MRS. SMALL *laugh; then, he adds in a manner which apparently is intended to sound humorous to* MRS. SMALL, *but has serious connotations for* TOM.*)* And make sure you don't *under*-charge her, either! *(*MRS. SMALL *titters again.* TOM *glances straight at his father; then, mutely proceeds to fill the order.)* He'll see to you now, Mrs. Small. I'm off for breakfast. I've been up since six this morning.

MRS. SMALL: Just fancy that! Early to bed and early to rise; makes a man healthy and wealthy and wise!

DALEY: Aye, that's a true word if there ever was one. Hear that, Tom?

TOM: Yes.

DALEY: It's in one ear and out the other with him. He'll have forgotten it by tomorrow, for sure.

MRS. SMALL: *(lifting a tin, as though she were toasting)* Here's hopin', Tom, you will live to be a hundred and make your million on the way!

TOM: *(muttering)* Just like Thomas Lipton.

DALEY: *(Turns sharply to* TOM *because of this uncalled-for remark.)* Get on with that order! Don't be keepin' Mrs. Small waiting! *(He goes into the living room.)*

MRS. SMALL: So you've finished with school now then, Tom?

TOM: Yes.

MRS. SMALL: And what are you goin' to do now, eh?

TOM: *(not particularly interested in discussing it with her)* Dunno. Serve in the shop with Dad, I suppose.

MRS. SMALL: A steady, easy job! People always have got to eat, haven't they?

TOM: I suppose so.

MRS. SMALL: *(leaning over and speaking confidentially)* I noticed Jean this mornin', bright as a berry, headin' in this direction—

TOM: *(writing the items on a list and ignoring her gossip)* Coffee, ham, peas—

MRS. SMALL: How much is that?

TOM: *(adds practically at a glance)* Seven and sixpence.

MRS. SMALL: Didn't take you long to add it! You sure it's right?

TOM: *(phlegmatically)* Want to check? *(He passes the list to her.)*

MRS. SMALL: *(laboriously adds; then:)* Mmm, it's right enough. *(She pays* TOM *the amount.)* There now! *(*TOM *hands her the parcel.)* Save us all from starvin'!

(With still another titter, MRS. SMALL *exits.* TOM *looks round the shop, sighs; then crosses to the window and looks out, presumably toward the docks where the mastheads of some ships tower over the roofs of the district's low houses. The lights dim in the shop. Simultaneously, they brighten in the living room.* DALEY *is seated at the table, having his breakfast.* AGNES*, dutifully, is serving him.)*

DALEY: He'll drive me daft! Sometimes I think I'll never make a businessman out of him—not in a hundred years! There's more drive, push and go in that clock than there is in him!

AGNES: Don't you think you might be a little too hard on the boy, Thomas?

DALEY: Too hard, is it? Rubbish, woman! It's you that are too *soft* with him! Always have been, and look what he's turning out like! Look at the sort of stuff he reads. I had a look at his books yesterday—not one on trade or business. Not one! And him havin' to make a living out of it. There was one in particular, *The Nigger of the Narcissus*. Now, what sort o' tripe is that? I'd been working for a wage four years when I was his age. And none of this nine-to-six caper, either! From seven in the morning till seven at night —at twelve years of age, mind you!

AGNES: *(unimpressed with his fragment from the repetitious* DALEY *saga)* Yes, dear. More tea?

DALEY: *(shoving his empty cup in front of her for a refill)* I'll give him *The Nigger of the Narcissus*!

AGNES: It isn't that sort of book at all.

DALEY: Uhh? And how would *you* be knowin'?

AGNES: He told me all about it. It's about the sea.

DALEY: About the sea then, is it? I'm not surprised! With him, it's the sea, sea, sea, all the time! It's enough to make me sick! *(He pauses for a moment as the joke blossoms in his mind.) Sea*-sick! *(He looks at* AGNES *for appreciation of his little gem.)*

AGNES: *(almost as though she hadn't heard)* Yes, dear.

DALEY: *(resuming)* If he'd spend half the time learning business that he spends on moonin' over ships, maybe he'd get somewhere! He's his Uncle Harry over again in many ways! He's got more like your looks, and some of your odd ways, but there's a lot of Harry in him. Same gormless, dreamy expression. Always readin'. Always out of this world! Harry was full of big dreams, too. Always goin' to do something fabulous!

AGNES: Well, Harry finally turned out pretty well after all.

DALEY: *(sourly)* And if he did, it was small credit to him. He'd never have done it by his own efforts, not him. He was one of the most shiftless characters I'd ever known!

AGNES: Oh, now—speaking of the dead that way!

DALEY: *(with revealing bitterness)* I tell you he was shiftless!

AGNES: Now, Thomas, he was your own brother. And he was good to us when we needed it.

DALEY: Ugh! In his position, that came easy! It was no

sacrifice—him havin' more than he knew what to do with! Aye, it was a lucky day for him, all right, when he met that broker's daughter. Though, what she saw in him to marry him for, I'll never know.

AGNES: He had charm, plenty of it.

DALEY: Charm! The stock-in-trade of rogues and no-goods! *(pause)* I'll see that the boy is able to earn his own living from trade even if I have to half kill him to train him!

AGNES: *(somberly)* Often in the night, Thomas, a fear comes over me, that he'll leave us—

DALEY: Leave? Him! Och, take no notice of his moonin' about ships!

AGNES: The sea seems to be drawing him away—

DALEY: He hasn't got the gumption to do anything more'n dream! For all his damn travel books, he's a home bird!

AGNES: *(in a small voice; almost to herself)* If he should go, somehow I can't imagine myself here without him—

DALEY: *(He looks up, amazed. He has never heard her speak this way before and despite his bluster, he appears uneasy.)* Nonsense, woman! There's nothin' that will drive our armchair wanderer farther away than the public library at the rim of the village!

(The lights dim in the living room, and rise once again in the shop. TOM *still stands gazing longingly out the window. The shop bell rings.* DANNY *enters. He is eighteen, and walks with a swagger appropriate to a man of the world of two years' standing. He wears an American-made leather jacket and tight jeans.* TOM*'s face brightens when he sees him.)*

DANNY: Hi, kid! Where's "Chunky" Tommy Lipton?

TOM: *(looking around, nervously)* He's having his breakfast.

DANNY: Taking time off for eating now? Does he want to die poor?

TOM: *(quickly, changing the subject)* I thought you were sailing today, Danny?

DANNY: Right, kid. On the evening tide. *Star of Bristol.* Bound for Capetown.

TOM: *(impressed) Capetown.* And after?

DANNY: Dunno, back home, I suppose. Maybe South America next trip. Buenos Aires—some place like that. Buenos noches, señorita! That's Spanish for "How's tricks, gal?" *(He lights a cigarette like one of the minor and tougher characters in a gangster film. He looks patronizingly around the small shop as he stamps the match out on the floor.)* Beats me, how you can stand being trapped in this place, lad! Now me— I'd suffocate in one day! *(leaning over counter)* Why don't you sneak down to the shipping office and pester 'em for a berth, way I did? They'll hand you one, just so's to get rid of you! *(He pokes* TOM *jovially.)*

TOM: Next year, maybe.

DANNY: Where's your courage, lad?

*(*TOM *is about to defend himself verbally, when the shop bell rings, the door opens, and* JEAN *comes in. She is a pleasant-looking girl; approximately* TOM*'s age. As soon as* TOM *sees* JEAN*, he tightens with nervousness.)*

DANNY: *(turning on the nautical charm)* Well, well, Jean! I'll trade my gunny sack if you don't get better-lookin' every time I return to port! *(with a wink)* I can see why Tom prefers the home life—

TOM: *(shyly)* Aw, cut it out, Danny!

JEAN *to* DANNY: Do you deliver the same routine in all the ports?

DANNY: It works, too! *(then, sidling up to* JEAN*)* But after all, I'm really a home-lovin' boy at heart—

JEAN: *(moving away)* Well, don't tell me. Tell your mother.

DANNY: *(starting)* Well, I've got to be gettin' on to make a few more calls 'fore sailing for Capetown.

TOM: Send a card from Capetown, Danny, will you? Something unusual, you know—*(quickly)* not women or any kind like that!

DANNY: Sure, lad. Maybe I'll get you a carving. How would that be?

TOM: That would be fine, thanks!

DANNY: O.K. Well, take it easy, eh? *(to* JEAN*)* I'll think of you every day, beautiful!

JEAN: Then for part of the time, at least, you'll be respectable.

DANNY: I wouldn't put any money on that!

(With a farewell wave, he makes as rugged an exit as possible. There is an awkward pause: TOM *and* JEAN, *left alone, suddenly become shy.)*

TOM: *(finally)* What wouldn't I give to be going on that trip!

JEAN: You could, Tom, if you set your mind to it.

TOM: *(scoffingly)* Sure, I'm such a forceful, dynamic type!

JEAN: *(steadily and emphatically, as if she realizes his need for support and self-confidence)* I believe you *could* do anything you set your mind to!

TOM: Were it so. . . . *(pause)*

JEAN: I've come to remind you about my birthday party tomorrow dusk.

TOM: I—I hadn't forgotten. I've got a bit of something for you. *(He gropes beneath the counter; brings up a parcel.)* Here! *(He hands it to her.)*

JEAN: Oh, Tom!

TOM: Open it!

JEAN: Before my birthday?

TOM: It's come a long way.

JEAN: *(Anxiously she opens the parcel: it is a beautifully worked Indian silk scarf. Breathlessly.)* Oh, Tom!

TOM: *(shyly)* Oh, it's nothing: got it from someone who'd been East last trip.

JEAN: *(draping the scarf over her shoulders)* I think this is the most beautiful present I've ever had!

TOM: *(flushed with pleasure at her delight)* It's nothing to what I'd like to buy. If I'd been there and had the money, I'd have brought back the best in silks and gold and silverwork. And even then I wouldn't be giving you anything half good enough!

*(*JEAN *gazes tenderly at him:* TOM *stands awkward and silent. Impetuously,* JEAN *moves toward him and kisses him. Just then,* DALEY *enters from the living-room. The two young people spring apart, but it is too late.* DALEY *takes in the scene. There is an ominous silence for a moment.)*

DALEY: So! This is your notion of looking after the shop? *(Silence)* Well?

JEAN: I was—just thanking Tom for my birthday present, Mr. Daley.

DALEY: *(sharply)* I think he's got a tongue of his own, young lady!

TOM: *(embarrassed in the presence of* JEAN*)* You heard what she said: I was giving her her present a day in advance!

DALEY: However you want to get rid of your money is your own affair! But in future, I don't want any of that sort of carry-on in the shop! *(He crosses to get some cigarettes).* I'd be obliged if you'd remember that, too, young lady!

JEAN: It was all very innocent, Mr. Daley.

DALEY: Och! Innocent, was it? *(He fixes* TOM *with a stare.* TOM'S *gaze drops.)* Now that you're done with your little relaxation, maybe you'll get round to checkin' that consignment of corned beef, as I ordered you? *(Once again,* TOM *is flattened.)* And you, young lady, would there be anything else that you'd be wantin'?

JEAN: *(after a second)* No.

DALEY: Well, then, don't interfere with progress! *(to* TOM*)* Look sharp about those tins, mind you! *(He returns to the living room with the cigarettes.)*

TOM: *(after* DALEY *has gone; wretchedly)* I gave a nice impressive performance, didn't I?

JEAN: I'd—better be going.

(The shop bell rings. A SAILOR *enters. He is in his early thirties, tanned, bright-eyed and as breezy as the weather which has given him his rugged, virile, outdoor look. He carries a small hold-all.)*

SAILOR: Hello Captain! Snug little berth you have here! *(eying* JEAN*)* And the fascinating items are not all on the shelves, I see!

TOM: *(to* JEAN, *as she makes a move to start)* I wish I were able to walk you home.

JEAN: *(tightening the scarf about her)* The scarf will accompany me home, Tom! *(*JEAN *hastens out.* TOM *gazes after her.)*

SAILOR: *(breaking the mood)* I can see that you're the

strong, silent type, me old bucko! And I bet you want to know why I'm here?

TOM: You want to buy something?

SAILOR: Ah, I can see there's no foxing a sharp 'un like you! As soon as I came in through that door, "Jack," I said to myself, "watch your pockets—we've got a cute 'un here!"

(TOM finally is taken in by the SAILOR's apparent good humour. He smiles.)

There, that's better! I thought you was afraid to smile on account that you didn't have your teeth in, but I see that you've got 'em in after all!

(TOM smiles even more broadly, reacting to the good-natured stranger, who grins back at him.)

Go ahead, Captain! Have a good laugh! Your face won't split and it's all part of the free service! *(pause)* Now you've found me out, I'll come clean and tell you what I want. *(TOM listens intently)* Down at the end of the street, two or three doors up from The Silver Bell, there's an old couple livin'. The old feller works as a watchman on the dock.

TOM: That would be Billy Ganns.

SAILOR: Billy Ganns it is! Well, now, Billy did me a good turn at the start of my last trip. He helped me on board when I was—let's say, when I was not myself?

TOM: *(understandingly)* Yes.

SAILOR: Ah, I thought you would understand by the wild devil-may-care look about you! What's your name, anyway, shipmate?

TOM: Tom.

SAILOR: Put it there, Tom. *(He offers his hand; self-consciously, TOM shakes it.)* I'm Jack. Now, Tom, what's the natural thing for a decent feller to do, eh?

TOM: For Billy Ganns?

SAILOR: Right!

TOM: Give him some sort of present, I suppose?

SAILOR: Sure, it is! And what sort of present would an old couple like that appreciate now? Besides a little vase from Kobe and a bottle of Chianti from Naples?

TOM: Food?

SAILOR: Ohh! You're a practical feller, Tom! We're going

to get on fine. Food it is, then! Now, it's in your hands. You're the expert! What do you suggest to start off with?

TOM: What about one of those big hams?

SAILOR: Should go down well!

(During the following scene, TOM *collects the various items of food, and places them on the counter.)*

TOM: And some salmon from British Columbia?

SAILOR: Vancouver the misty? Why not! Let's have a few tins.

TOM: There's corned beef from the Argentine.

SAILOR: Pass one over, then! Buenos Aires—the biggest city in the Southern Hemisphere. Not the most beautiful, by a long way, but the biggest by far!

TOM: *(distantly)* I should think Rio would be the most beautiful.

SAILOR: I think you're right, Tom! That bumpy ring of hills around the bay will take a lot of beating. Let's have some coffee on the strength of it! Now, what have we got in the way of fruit?

TOM: Grapefruit from South Africa?

SAILOR: Fetch a couple of those, eh? The Table Mountain is one of my favourites. What's in those yellow tins by the window?

TOM: Pineapple. From Australia. Queensland, I suppose.

SAILOR: Queensland, it is! You seem to know a bit about these places, Tom. Are you interested in travel?

TOM: *(attempting to convey by the tone of his voice just how far short the word "interested" describes his obsession)* Interested?!

(The SAILOR *looks at* TOM *silently for a moment. He seems to see through the lad and his situation, and from now until the end of the scene, there is a current of understanding and compassion in his attitude toward the boy.)*

TOM: I've never wanted to do anything else. But all I've done is read about it.

SAILOR: That's as good a start as any. When I was a kid I used to be the same. When the time comes that you are ready to go—you'll go!

TOM: But how can you tell when you're ready?

SAILOR: I dunno. You just know, that's all. When the

time comes you'll be able to tell, all right, and that will be it.

TOM: I've got a friend, Danny, not much older than me, and he's been at sea two years now—

SAILOR: How old are you, Tom?

TOM: Sixteen.

SAILOR: That's nothing to worry about, then, Tom! I was twenty when I went.

TOM: *(in shocked surprise)* As old as that?

SAILOR: Aye, though when you get to it, twenty doesn't seem any great age.

TOM: *(embarrassed, for fear he has hurt the* SAILOR'S *feelings)* I didn't mean it that way.

SAILOR: *(laughs) That's all right! (studies the label on the pineapple tin)* They look harmless enough in tins, don't they. But you should try cutting the beggars!

TOM: *(fascinated)* You've worked on a pineapple farm?

SAILOR: *(nods)* Got paid off in Sydney once, and went up north to put in a season on the sugar cane and the pineapples. When you get to Australia, Tom, take my advice—if you don't mind my giving it—

TOM: I'd be glad to—get your advice—

SAILOR: Stay well away from the cane and the pineapples, unless you're really short of money, because they're murder!

TOM: I'll remember. When I get there.

SAILOR: See that you do!

TOM: *(in a sudden burst of confidence)* I think that the place I'd like to see most of all is India.

SAILOR: Yes, quite a place! Beautiful temples. Cows all over. Crowds. It's an interesting place, all right! Smelly, mark you, but teeming with life. How about a couple of packets of tea on the strength of it? Talking about crowds, China's got 'em! Hong Kong and Canton; now there's a spot, Tom, Canton! Up-river from the docks, from shore to shore, there's nothing but houseboats—sampans, they call 'em. You can see the kids jumping into the river off one. And from the next they might be tossing in their rubbish and a little farther up, you might see 'em drawing up water to drink!

TOM: *(completely swept away by the traveller's tale)* But isn't that unhealthy?

SAILOR: *(wryly)* I shouldn't be a bit surprised. Why, isn't that China tea you've got there?

TOM: Yes. We've got most kinds of tea.

SAILOR: How's that, Tom?

TOM: My father's a great admirer of Tom Lipton.

SAILOR: Is he now? Old Tom was a great sailor, too. Guess you father's interested in ships, too, eh?

TOM: *(with the unconscious natural bitterness that creeps into his voice in any discussion of his father)* No, not him.

SAILOR: Well, pass over a sample of that China tea, then, and let's hope its healthier than their water! *(He surveys the mound of provisions which* TOM *has placed upon the counter.)* Well, now, how much is this lot?

*(*TOM *begins to calculate as the* SAILOR *lights up a cigarette.)*

Smoke, Tom?

TOM: *(glancing toward the living-room entrance)* No, thanks, not in the shop. *(Then, suddenly, almost in defiance)* Yes! I think I will. *(He takes a cigarette from the* SAILOR's *package, lights it, then puffing away, returns to his addition.)* Did you ever see the Barrier Reef?

SAILOR: The Great Barrier Reef in Australia?

TOM:*(nods)* Mmm.

SAILOR: Never did, but it's something I've always wanted to see.

TOM: Me, too.

SAILOR: Who knows? One day, Tom, we'll both be seeing it, God willing.

TOM: *(He has completed his calculations.)* That's one pound eighteen and seven.

SAILOR: *(empties his pockets)* One quid eleven and three. Will you take a cheque, then?

TOM: *(hesitating)* I wouldn't mind. But Dad says no.

SAILOR: *(thinks for a moment)* I'll tell you what I'll do. *(He gropes in his case.)* See this? *(He brings out a small, beautifully carved Chinese junk in a bottle. He holds it aloft.)* I got this in Hong Kong. Worth anything from three quid up. I'll give you thirty bob and this and we'll call it square. How does that sound to you, shipmate?

TOM: *(breathlessly, as he takes the Chinese treasure)* She's a beauty!

SAILOR: Knew you had good taste, Tom!

TOM: *(once again hesitant)* But Dad. . . . *(then, a sudden thought)* I'll buy it from you myself and put my own money in—only—how much do you want for it?

SAILOR: How much do you suggest now?

TOM: I've got eleven bob. But if that isn't enough, maybe I could borrow some by tomorrow, say, if you could come back then?

SAILOR: Let's say ten bob! I never was much good at complicated sums of money.

TOM: Ten bob? But it's worth more—a lot more—*(He fondles the treasure.)*

SAILOR: That's just about what I paid for it. So, ten bob it is!

*(*TOM *hastily adjusts the small change on the counter and stammers his thanks.)*

Let's hope she brings you luck and sails with you!

TOM: *(busily packing the provisions into a cardboard carton)* She will bring me luck, I know!

*(*TOM *hands the carton to the* SAILOR, *as* DALEY *emerges from the living-room. The* SAILOR *adjusts the carton under his arm, nods pleasantly at* DALEY, *and then starts for the door.* DALEY *watches with a strange curiosity.)*

SAILOR: *(with a salute to* TOM*) So-long, mate!*

TOM: So-long! Good luck, mate!

(The SAILOR *leaves.* DALEY *slowly crosses to the rear of the counter.)*

DALEY: Getty pretty chummy with strangers, aren't you? Do that too often and you'll find that you'll be gypped one day!

(He notices the list of purchases; stops to scrutinize it. Then he glances at the money on the counter which TOM *has not had the time to deposit in the till.)*

What's this? There's ten shillings missing!

TOM: Not really.

DALEY: *(angrily)* What do you mean, "not really?" Do you think I'm blind—can't count? There's ten shillings missing I say! So, that's how the books have been out, is it? This is where the money's been trickling to! But this time you've slipped—

TOM: That's a lie!

(DALEY *straightens, shocked by* TOM'S *sudden strength.)*

Do you really think I'd sneak about taking a few piddling bob here and there? Do you think I haven't got any pride at all?

DALEY: *(suddenly on the defence)* There's ten bob missing! That's fact enough, isn't it?

TOM: I can explain!

DALEY: Well, let me hear you, lad!

TOM: I—he didn't have cash enough for the whole amount—

DALEY: So?

TOM: So, I bought something from him for the difference and I was going to put the ten bob, from my own money, into the till.

DALEY: You were, were you? And what did you buy off him?

(TOM *brings the ship model into sight and his delight in it is shown by the way he handles it. His father notices this. He inspects the object and grunts.)*

You accepted this rubbish instead of ten bob?

TOM: It's not rubbish! If you knew about this sort of thing, you'd know that it was worth more, much more—

DALEY: *(aroused)* No, I don't know about this sort of thing! I only know about running a business in a business-like way, which is something you'll never learn if you live to be a hundred! What sort of business practice is this, you fool, to be takin' rubbish like this instead of cash! Do you want to make me a laughing-stock about the district?!

TOM: I tell you, it's *not* rubbish!

DALEY: And it's not business either!

TOM: *(tensely)* I told you, I'd pay for it with my own money!

DALEY: *(scornfully)* Your own money! The only money you've ever had is the money *I've* given you! Remember that!!

TOM: I'll remember! Now, for the last time, I'll pay you back!

DALEY: *(furiously)* I'll say you'll pay it back! And here's for you to remember the lesson!!

(He throws the ship model onto the floor and stamps on it. TOM, *stunned, slowly stoops down and picks up the pieces. As he straightens, something in him appears to be just as shattered as the ship model.* DALEY *realizes that this time he has gone too far and tries vainly to look truculent as* TOM *takes a steady look at him.)*

TOM: *(quietly, and although his voice is a bit shaken, there is no hate in it)* You poor miserable devil!

(TOM *removes his apron, flings it onto the counter, and starts toward the front door.* DALEY *is far more shattered by the quiet contempt than he would have been by any surface display of bitterness. He makes one last, desperate attempt to assert superiority, but his voice lacks the old authoritative ring and has an undercurrent of fear in it.)*

DALEY: Where are you going?

TOM: *(stopping at the door and turning back)* First, down to the shipping office. And then—anywhere! As long as it's far away. I just don't want to be like you or Tom Lipton or anyone else! I want to be *myself*! I'll seek and find my own model!

DALEY: *(coming forward)* All very fine, I'm sure! But what are you going to use for money?

TOM: I'll earn it. My way! You want to be repaid, don't you?

DALEY: And your mother?

TOM: *(tenderly)* I'll write to her—she'll always know where I''ll be.

DALEY: *(threateningly)* You go out that door—you needn't come to me ever again for anything!

TOM: *(simply, yet with a ring of confidence in his voice)* I don't expect to. *(He goes out through the shop door.)*

DALEY: *(calls, desperately)* Come back here! You hear

me? Tom! Come back this instant! Tom! Come back! Tom!!

(TOM *disappears as the Curtain comes slowly down.)*

PRODUCTION

SET CONSTRUCTION may appear to be a less glamorous job than acting, directing or designing, but a production's chief *carpenter,* in charge of carrying out the instructions of the set designer, can by his efficiency and ingenuity—or by the lack of them—ruin even the best performances, direction and set designs.

1/ How is the set for "Ship of Dreams" more complex than those for the Saroyan and Wilder plays?

2/ Doors pose special problems for the workman who is to construct the set. Why?

How many doors are there in the set for "Ship of Dreams"?

3/ The division of the stage into two sections could be eliminated if the theatre were equipped with a revolving stage.

Is it more or less effective that the two rooms of the play's set be constantly before the audience, even though one of them is in darkness? Why?

4/ What vital role do the painters have in completing the set for Hughes' play?

What colours would you choose as dominant ones for each of the two rooms? Why?

STAGE LIGHTING carefully planned can greatly enhance the atmosphere of a play. Three sets of lights form the basis of most stage lighting systems: lights above the stage and behind the set (to light the stage and to illuminate *backdrops,* at the rear of the stage, such as "the panoramic view" of the district in which the Daley store is located); footlights to focus the audience's attention on the actors; and spotlights to illuminate certain actions and characters.

1/ Why is stage lighting especially important in Hughes' play?

What colours would you choose to emphasize in lighting the Daleys' shop and their living room? Why?

2/ Spotlights, focusing on only a small portion of the stage can heighten the impact of a certain situation.

What action might be effectively spotlit in this play? Why might a director want such a special effect?

REVIEW

Critics' comments are usually knowledgeable ones, supported by definite references and as free as possible from emotional bias; these writers know the influence their opinions might have on a play's financial success.

The ordinary theatre-goer, however, usually makes his own informal judgment of a play. Suppose that you are in the lobby of a theatre after the performance of "Ship of Dreams." Imagine what comments each of the following people would make on the play:

1. A successful, middle-aged businessman
2. A wife, usually dominated by her husband
3. A teen-age boy
4. A teen-age girl
5. A psychologist or a psychiatrist.

RESEARCH

All the audience usually sees on stage is a troupe of actors performing within the limits of the stage setting. Often, though, the playwright wants his audience to imagine scenes beyond the confines of the set.

1/ The playwright must, of course, first convince us that we are viewing *a real scene.*

What references to the city and its immediate vicinity help us to anchor ourselves securely in Cardiff, Wales?

How are these geographical details incorporated into the dialogue of the characters?

2/ Sometimes, as in this play, the author wants us to consider what is happening on stage *and* what is going on faraway, often, from the setting of the play.

What geographical details in the play remind us that there is a vast world beyond the walls of the Daley house?

Why is it important that this other world be brought to the audience's attention?

3/ Recently playwrights and directors have made skilful use of projectuals—*images flashed on screens above or beside the stage.*

At what points in the action of "Ship of Dreams" might such projectuals increase the impact of certain scenes in this play? Why?

READING

1/ Joseph Conrad's *The Nigger of the Narcissus,* which Tom was reading the night before the action of "The Ship of Dreams" begins, is available in a Dell paperback edition (LE 6362) and is probably on your school's library shelves.

Read Conrad's novel and decide why its hero captured Tom's interest. In what way is the *Narcissus* also a "ship of dreams"?

2/ Consult a biographical dictionary such as the *Dictionary of National Biography* for details of Sir Thomas Lipton's career as a businessman and the importance the sea played in his life. Why is he a logical figure over which father and son might quarrel?

How do each of these characters reveal their own prejudices in their reactions to Lipton?

3/ A sampling of other one-act plays by Canadian authors can be found in *Curtain Rising,* edited by W. S. Milne (Longmans, 1958), and *Canada on Stage,* edited by Stanley Richards (Clarke Irwin, 1960). How many of the authors, like Hughes, were not native Canadians?

PROTEST NORMAN WILLIAMS

REHEARSAL

STAGE MAKE-UP

Television commercials continually bombard us with appeals to use various cosmetics to beautify the face and the hands. The make-up artist uses cosmetics on actors' faces and hands, too, but his concern may not be the creation of an illusion of health and beauty; in fact he may sometimes be aiming for an opposite effect. His job is to help the playwright and the actor *to project the physical appearance of a character* across the gap that separates the actor from his audience.

1/ You are asked to do the make-up for an actress who is to portray a *grandmother.*

What details of her physical appearance would you concentrate on? Why?

2/ The next character you are asked to do the make-up for is the *mother* of the family.

Describe briefly how you would emphasize the difference in appearance between the mother and the grandmother.

3/ The teen-age daughter of the family is your next challenge as make-up artist.

How would you emphasize her *youth?*

4/ Why do you have to pay attention to the make-up you use on the *hands* as well as the faces of these actors?

How is the make-up artist's work complicated if all three of the actresses are to portray Oriental characters?

The make-up artist has been rehearsing, too, to achieve the right effect for these three actresses and the father of the family who appear on stage in Norman Williams' "Protest."

Short Plays for Reading + Acting 1970

Protest NORMAN WILLIAMS

Characters

THE GRANDMOTHER   THE FATHER

THE MOTHER   THE DAUGHTER

Scene: The time is 1900.
The setting is the main room of a Japanese home. It is bright and airy with walls consisting of light-coloured wooden panels. There are entrances at left, at right, and at centre back. In the back wall, left of centre, is a gilded Buddhist shrine. To the right and down-stage are the low black tables and cushions which represent the dining furniture of the Japanese household. To the left and looking incongruously out of place is the only piece of Western furniture in the room, a plain wooden chair. At front, left, are two floor cushions.

The stage is momentarily empty. Then, from centre back, the GRANDMOTHER *enters. She is a tiny, dignified lady of advanced years. She carries a bowl and crosses the room to add it to those already on the tables. As she bends to do so, she catches sight of the chair, left, drops the dish with a crash and retreats with a shrill shriek towards centre back.*

GRANDMOTHER: *(calling)* Daughter! Daughter! Come here! Come here!

MOTHER: *(enters hurriedly from the back)* What's the matter? What is it?

GRANDMOTHER: *(clutches her and points to the chair)* That? What is that?

MOTHER: *(detaches herself and goes gingerly towards the chair)* I'm—not sure. I've never seen one before—

GRANDMOTHER: *(shrieks)* Don't go too close! Be careful. Be careful!

MOTHER: It's all right, Mother. *(She moves closer.)*

GRANDMOTHER: Oh, the merciful Buddha protect you.

MOTHER: *(curious)* I *believe* I know what it is. *(She is very close to it now. The* GRANDMOTHER *is trembling and close to sobbing.)*

GRANDMOTHER: Oh, take care. Take care!

MOTHER: *(bending low and peering under the chair)* Yes, I'm sure. It's a chair.

GRANDMOTHER: What is—a—chair? What is it for?

MOTHER: To sit on. I've heard them described.

GRANDMOTHER: To sit on? What kind of beast would seat itself on a hideous thing like that?

MOTHER: Men, Mother; men sit on them.

GRANDMOTHER: I don't believe it. Only evil spirits would sit on a devilish device like that. *(The* MOTHER *puts out her hand to touch it.)* Don't touch it. Oh, don't touch it!

MOTHER: *(drawing back; a trifle nervously)* It's only made of wood.

GRANDMOTHER: Evil and sorcery reside in wood as well as in anything else.

(Enter the FATHER *from right. The* MOTHER *and* GRANDMOTHER *return his bow.)*

FATHER: Did I hear someone shriek? I wasn't properly dressed or I would have come before now to see what the trouble was.

GRANDMOTHER: I shrieked! There are devils in the house, and we are all at the mercy of evil!

FATHER: What's this, my esteemed mother? Devils? Evil?

GRANDMOTHER: There! *(She points an accusing finger at the chair.)*

FATHER: A chair.

MOTHER: I *told* you it was a chair.

FATHER: Where did it come from?

MOTHER: We don't know. It wasn't here a short time ago; I have been in and out putting the bowls on the table.

FATHER: *(crosses to it, wonderingly)* A chair. In our house.

MOTHER: You have seen one before, my husband?

FATHER: I have seen them in Tokyo.

MOTHER: Are they made in Tokyo?

FATHER: *(laughs)* No, they come from the Western countries. The Western barbarians sit on them all the time.

GRANDMOTHER: Didn't I say they were from the devil?

FATHER: Here is how they do it. *(He is about to sit in the chair as the* GRANDMOTHER, *as if pursued by seven devils, runs wailing out of the room, centre back.)*

MOTHER: Oh, you have really frightened her now.

FATHER: *(seriously)* That was wickedly unfilial of me. I apologize. *(He bows.)*

MOTHER: *(lowering her eyes)* I should not have pointed out that you had.

FATHER: You were quite correct. It is right for you to point out my blunders. You know I have always been liberal in matters such as that.

(A sound of sobbing is heard, off.)

MOTHER: I'm afraid your poor mother is crying with fright.

FATHER: I will reassure her. *(Secretly, with mischief.)* But, just before I do, here is how they do it! *(He lets his seat rest for just a few moments on the chair and then jumps up. But the sight of him even that briefly in this unaccustomed posture is too much for the* MOTHER. *She bursts into laughter as he crosses to centre back.)*

MOTHER: You look like a duck.

FATHER: *(calling softly)* Mother. *(The sobbing, off, hesitates, ceases. Calls again.)* Mother, your unworthy son is calling you.

GRANDMOTHER: *(off)* What is it, my revered son?

FATHER: I send my humble respects to my aged mother and apologize in the dust for frightening her.

GRANDMOTHER: You are—a good son, and I know you wouldn't frighten me purposely.

FATHER: Will you return to us now?

GRANDMOTHER: Are you sitting on—"it"?

FATHER: No, my mother.

GRANDMOTHER: Are you going to sit on it?

FATHER: No, my mother.
GRANDMOTHER: Are you *touching* it?
FATHER: No.
GRANDMOTHER: Are you going to touch it?
FATHER: No.
GRANDMOTHER: Has it been removed from the room?
FATHER: No.
GRANDMOTHER: It is not a good influence in the room. It should be removed.
FATHER: Do you want me to touch it?
GRANDMOTHER: No! No! Don't touch it!
FATHER: Then how am I to remove it, revered Mother?

(The GRANDMOTHER *appears up-stage.)*

GRANDMOTHER: If we pray to the Buddha, he will remove it.
FATHER: I wish I knew how it got here.
MOTHER: It must *belong* to someone.
FATHER: But to whom?

(At this, the DAUGHTER, *a lovely, proud-looking girl of seventeen enters quickly from left. She stands facing them.)*

DAUGHTER: *(defiantly)* It is mine!
FATHER: } Yours!
MOTHER: }
GRANDMOTHER: *(crossing towards her but wary of the chair)* Yours? It was you who brought this sorcerer's instrument into the home of your parents? You who set it down before the shrine of the sacred Buddha?
DAUGHTER: *(calmly)* Yes, it was.
GRANDMOTHER: *(stretching out her arms to the Buddha)* Have compassion on the house where evil enters in the hands of its only daughter.
MOTHER: How could you do such a thing? Aren't you ashamed?
FATHER: *(quietly)* Revered Mother, will you please your son by going to your room to prepare for the evening meal?
GRANDMOTHER: *(dropping her arms, looking old and weary)* I will go. *(She moves slowly across and out, right. The* MOTHER *and* FATHER *bow to her.)*
MOTHER: Yes, honoured Mother-in-law, go and prepare

for your evening meal, and we will take care of this affair.

FATHER: And, my wife, if we are to have supper someone must be in the kitchen to prepare it.

MOTHER: That is so. *(She bows submissively and exits upstage.)*

(The FATHER *walks to the chair and sits down. The* DAUGHTER *stands unmoving in her original position.)*

FATHER: It's not a very comfortable chair, is it?

DAUGHTER: *We* aren't used to sitting in chairs.

FATHER: That is true. Still, I have done so before. *(The* DAUGHTER *shows interest.)* In the big cities they are quite commonly seen. But they aren't plain wooden ones like this. Some of them I have seen are made of shining brown cow-hide; cool to the touch and so slippery I would be afraid to sit in one. Others are huge affairs with springs in the seat, and when you sit down it would seem you are sinking into a deep, soft cloud. I imagine the Westerners use them for sleeping. At least the ones I saw seated in them seemed on the verge of sleep.

DAUGHTER: Oh, there are so many things I have *never* seen.

FATHER: That is true of most of us, and many of the things we never see are right before our eyes all the time.

DAUGHTER: I didn't mean *those* things. I mean the new, wonderful things the Westerners have.

FATHER: *(rises and takes the chair out, left)* I will put this into the "shoe-off" room; it disturbs your grandmother.

DAUGHTER: And may I keep it in my room?

FATHER: We will have to think about that.

DAUGHTER: Ishimoto said it was a very fine chair and that houses in America have twenty or thirty each in them.

FATHER: *(returns from left)* So it was Ishimoto who gave you the chair? I guessed it was.

DAUGHTER: He didn't give it to me. I bought it.

FATHER: How could you buy it? You have no money. *(The* FATHER *seats himself on one of the cushions, left.)*

DAUGHTER: I paid him with two of my pearl haircombs,

my writing brush, and the red sash I had at the New Year.

FATHER: And that is how Ishimoto grows richer day by day. Sit down here opposite me, and let us talk together as we used to when you were a child. *(The* DAUGHTER *seats herself on the cushion opposite him.)* It is here, on this very spot, your old teacher used to teach you your lessons. Don't you remember any longer, with any fondness, all that he told you of our Japanese past, our culture and our wise men, our traditions, and the courageous lives of our history's heroines?

DAUGHTER: I only remember one thing about those lessons, my father.

FATHER: And what is that?

DAUGHTER: That all the two hours my old teacher sat where you sit now and droned into my ear our Japanese past, I was made to sit motionless, so: *(She assumes the rigid posture of the Japanese student.)* Never once was I allowed to move an arm, a hand, or my littlest finger. How the minutes dragged on! I thought he would never finish, that I would turn to stone on the spot and never be able to move again, or run and play in the courtyard.

FATHER: It is true the discipline was harsh—

DAUGHTER: One day, I remember, I felt my left foot grow numb and I ventured to move my trunk the tiniest fraction to relieve the pressure on it. My teacher saw me; he gave me a look like the black God of War. Without a word to me, he stopped the lesson; he got up and left without a bow. I could hear him in the next room complaining loudly to you and saying how unworthy I was. I was left crying with fear and shame.

FATHER: I remember.

DAUGHTER: From that day on, I had my lessons from him in the outer room with no heat, although it was December and the snow was piled high in the streets. I would turn purple with the cold, but dared not shiver or tremble in the slightest.

FATHER: Yes, yes. Your mother and I discussed it through an entire night.

DAUGHTER: I didn't know you noticed . . . or cared.

FATHER: We did. We were afraid it would be too hard on you but we decided, in the dawn light, rightly or wrongly, that discipline was the path to wisdom and virtue. We wanted our daughter to be wise and virtuous. We followed custom.

DAUGHTER: Custom!

FATHER: I know you think custom ancient and barbaric.

DAUGHTER: Yes, I do.

FATHER: Yet it is not. It does not diminish men's actions. It gives those actions form. It is our way of respecting others.

DAUGHTER: But it never changes. *(proudly)* This is the year 1900, you know.

FATHER: *(amused)* A Western year. 1900, eh? Did Mr. Ishimoto give you that information? Perhaps free, with the chair?

DAUGHTER: *(with child-like mysteriousness)* Oh, I had heard what year it was.

FATHER: Will you believe me if I tell you something?

DAUGHTER: I will try.

FATHER: It is not true that custom fails to change.

DAUGHTER: I don't see that it does.

FATHER: You have not observed it long enough. Do you know there was a day when meat was never eaten in this house? To eat meat was looked upon as a loathsome evil because the Buddha himself forbade the killing of animals. But gradually the belief began to change. Little by little we were invaded by new ideas from the Western world. I well remember the day I first ordered the preparation of meat in this house. My honoured mother spent that day in her room at her personal shrine praying for all of us who dared to break a tradition over a thousand years old. She ate nothing for three days and for two years and more would not eat with us in this room or go near the kitchen where the meat was prepared. To this very hour she has never tasted it and will not if she lives another hundred years.

DAUGHTER: She is stubborn.

FATHER We must all be stubborn in what we believe or one day find we believe in nothing.

DAUGHTER: But you said you change your beliefs.

FATHER: I do, and have, and will. When others began to eat meat, I said to myself: Is there some good in this? And I inquired and found there was; that animal flesh makes men stronger and builds muscles to withstand cold and hard work. And so I said, "I will change. We will eat meat in my house." And we did. But not until I had considered it carefully and weighed the custom against the new belief.

DAUGHTER: Perhaps you have changed—in small things.

FATHER: Small things?

DAUGHTER: Eating meat is a small thing to me when I see how chained our lives are.

FATHER: We are not chained. We are civilized and reserved, it is true—

DAUGHTER: You call it civilized and reserved, but I call it a prison. I am in a prison and I yearn to be free.

(Enter MOTHER *at centre back. She carries a bowl, crosses to the table and places the bowl on it. She putters about as an excuse for eavesdropping.)*

FATHER : Free to do as you please?

DAUGHTER: Free to do as—

FATHER: As—what?

DAUGHTER: As other women do.

FATHER: What other women?

DAUGHTER: Western women.

FATHER: Ishimoto!

DAUGHTER: Mr. Ishimoto has told me many things; he has painted me a picture of another world—a world I long to know and be a part of. In that world, women are free to grow and blossom instead of sitting with folded hands and allowing life to slip away from them as they do here.

FATHER: Women here live honourable lives.

DAUGHTER: *(flatly)* They obey their husbands and bear children and die with never a question on their lips.

FATHER: Is that not honourable?

DAUGHTER: It is not freedom. In the Western lands women

do not hide behind shutters and sit in an eternal twilight while others regulate their lives.

FATHER: They do not?

DAUGHTER: No. There they walk freely on the streets or go into tea-houses alone and order what they wish and pay for it themselves, for they have their own money.

FATHER: I have heard of that.

DAUGHTER: But, most important, they go to school and learn what men learn. They talk to men as their equals and, Mr. Ishimoto says, a wife may even criticize her husband.

(The MOTHER, *who has listened in growing horror, utters an exclamation at this and hurriedly leaves the room.)*

FATHER: My daughter—

DAUGHTER: And it is said that men embrace their wives in front of others and show affection in ways I don't properly understand. But I know it is by more than a bow.

FATHER: It is. I have heard of it. It is called kissing.

DAUGHTER: That's it. That is what Mr. Ishimoto called it.

FATHER: But a kiss is only another custom, strange to us but familiar to them. There is as much feeling of the heart in a bow as there is in a kiss. And yet, to my mind, a bow is in good form because it is an unselfish recognition of another; while a kiss, which is part of love-making, shows a desire for one's own pleasure.

DAUGHTER: It sounds exciting and natural to me.

FATHER: What is natural and what is not? It would seem that all of life must be regulated in some way if we are to live together. One could argue that it is "natural" to have customs to regulate "naturalness".

DAUGHTER: *(boldly, then hesitatingly)* I think it is natural for—

FATHER: For what?

DAUGHTER: For a girl to choose her own husband.

FATHER: *(rises)* What do you say? Oh, this is too much. I have sat here patiently trying to reason with you, but this is too much.

DAUGHTER: I don't want to marry a man I've never seen.

FATHER: Ungrateful, unfilial child! What do you know, what does any young girl know about choosing a husband? What can she know of his means, his family, his character, his education, which are what matter in a husband?

DAUGHTER: I *won't*! I *won't* marry him.

FATHER: I draw the line. Finally and firmly. Have all the romantic day-dreams you like—no doubt your husband will pay for them—but you *will* marry the man we have chosen for you.

DAUGHTER: *(beating her hands on the floor)* No, no, no, no.

FATHER: This is my fault. I should have supervised your education.

DAUGHTER: *(sobbing)* Education.

FATHER: But the education of a daughter is always in the hands of the women of the house.

DAUGHTER: *(triumphantly)* There, you see? Another *custom*!

(Enter the MOTHER, *who brings more bowls to the table. She arranges the cushions and exits right.)*

FATHER: Come. Pick yourself up. Our meal is ready.

(The DAUGHTER *rises and wipes her eyes on her sleeve. The* FATHER *takes up a position before the gilded shrine. Enter* MOTHER *and* GRANDMOTHER *from right. They cross and take up positions behind the* FATHER. *The* DAUGHTER *occupies the final position. At last they are in a row the shape of a semicircle.)*

FATHER: Lord Buddha, Light of Heaven and Earth, giver of Eternal Life, all-wise and merciful, look upon your humble servants and receive their gratitude for your compassionate gift of food. *(He bows low to the shrine and moves to the right towards the table.)*

(The GRANDMOTHER *then bows a deep and reverent bow, going down on her knees to do so. The* MOTHER *bows deeply from the waist. They move away to the right.)*

(The DAUGHTER *gives a brief and perfunctory bow and joins the rest.)*

(They seat themselves at the table, the FATHER *first in*

accordance with precedence, and begin their meal. There is silence for several moments.)

DAUGHTER: Father!

FATHER:
MOTHER:
GRANDMOTHER: } Shhhhhhh!

(silence for a few moments)

DAUGHTER: *(puts down her bowl, in suppressed emotion)* I can't—

GRANDMOTHER: *(flatly)* It is not proper to speak at meals. *(There is silence again as the* DAUGHTER *fidgets and frets, growing more despairing as the silent moments pass.)*

MOTHER: *(in a whisper)* Don't fidget, daughter. You are disturbing everyone. Calm and tranquillity at meal-time—

DAUGHTER: Oh, none of you care, none of you care. My heart could be breaking and you would sit there eating silently like cows because it is the custom. *(She rises quickly.)*

MOTHER: Daughter! What are you doing?

GRANDMOTHER: The sacred Buddha protect us! She has risen from the table.

MOTHER: Child, child, think what you are doing. No woman rises from her cushion before the master of the household and then only when all are finished. It is an iron rule.

FATHER: I rise, too. *(bows to the* GRANDMOTHER *and* MOTHER*)* I beg your forgiveness. *(They return his bow. He gets up and goes towards the* DAUGHTER.) Are you completely mad? Have you no respect left at all for your revered mother and your honoured grand-mother? Remember, your ideas aren't the only ideas in the world, and while you are in your father's house—

DAUGHTER: *(interrupting)* How long will I *be* in it?

GRANDMOTHER:
MOTHER: } *(in horror)* She has interrupted him.

(They hide their faces.)

DAUGHTER: In a year, a little year, I shall go to some strange house and sit upon the bridal couch with downcast eyes, waiting for a stranger to come and claim me for his slave. I will *not* do it. I will not. I will show you. *(She runs quickly away and out, left.)*

FATHER: *(turns back to the table and bows again to the two women)* We shall continue our meal. *(He sits and they eat silently.)*

(After a few moments there is a sound of sobbing off, left. Those at the table give no indication they hear.)

(Enter, DAUGHTER *from left, much transformed and near to hysteria. She has let down her sleek, black hair from its coils and has cut it down to short and jagged lengths. Her gown is covered with hair and she is cutting what lengths remain as she enters.)*

DAUGHTER: There! Now he will not marry me, whoever he is.

(The three at the table have, in spite of their control, looked at the DAUGHTER *and a kind of paralysis has overcome them at the shocking sight. The* FATHER *has half risen, the* GRANDMOTHER *has hidden her face, the* MOTHER's *hands are held up as if to ward off a blow.)*

FATHER: *(bows hastily to the* MOTHER *and* GRANDMOTHER*)* I must rise. *(They bow to him. He rises and faces the* DAUGHTER.*)*

DAUGHTER: *(in her sobs)* You see, I meant what I said.

FATHER: You have cut your hair! As a widow would do.

DAUGHTER: Yes, like a widow.

FATHER: This is madness.

DAUGHTER: And if it grows in before my wedding day, I shall pull it out by the roots.

FATHER: Wicked child.

DAUGHTER: No superstitious man would marry me now, looking like a widow, for fear he would die. And they are all superstitious and—stupid *(She exits left. The* GRANDMOTHER *has risen, shaking and trembling, from her cushion. She makes her way across the room to the shrine in the desperate, plodding fashion of a wanderer athirst in the desert who sights an oasis.)*

GRANDMOTHER: I must regain my tranquillity. *(She kneels*

before the Buddha and is motionless during the following:)

MOTHER: *(still seated)* My Husband!

FATHER: Yes.

MOTHER: Is this—my fault? Some fault of mine?

FATHER: No, it is mine. How could you know of all the new ideas abroad in our country or how they might change your daughter from day to day, tearing her from the old ways?

MOTHER: If she does not marry him, there will be great shame on our family name.

FATHER: It will be remembered from generation to generation.

MOTHER: Could she not be forced to marry him?

FATHER: She could be.

(The GRANDMOTHER *rises and comes to them.)*

GRANDMOTHER: She is not a child to be forced. She would only grow more rebellious and by her unwifely actions bring shame to our good name after her marriage.

MOTHER: What are we to do?

GRANDMOTHER: *(despairingly)* Oh, the old, safe ways are crumbling. In my day, tradition and discipline gave women strength in their duty and joy in their lives. But now, the scourge has spread across the land, destroying the ancient virtues of humility and modesty. Have you not seen, even here, how some women hurry along the paths at an unseemly rate until they are walking like men?

MOTHER: I have seen that.

GRANDMOTHER: They no longer arrange flowers in the classical manner but place them in the vase as if they were growing in natural chaos.

FATHER: It is so.

GRANDMOTHER: They neglect to subdue their voices when they speak and fail to bow to their elders at the proper times—oh, it is all around us—all around us—and now it has struck our home.

FATHER: It is my fault. Not to have protected her from these influences was a great fault in me.

GRANDMOTHER: Forgive my rude contradiction, but the fault is ours.

MOTHER: Yes, it is ours. In our hands she was moulded.

GRANDMOTHER: More particularly, the fault is mine. As the eldest, it was my duty to conserve in her the traditions of my life and the order of my discipline.

FATHER: Don't blame yourselves. I do not blame you. The forces from without, which have come like hurricanes from across the sea, are powerful. Hardly a home has not felt them.

GRANDMOTHER: We are as powerful as they. We understand how to sacrifice to save all we hold precious. As in the past, sacrifices were made—as in the past.

FATHER: My revered mother—

GRANDMOTHER: Does the child love me?

MOTHER: There is no doubt of that. Ever since she was a child and you brought her pears from the orchard, carved her pumpkin at the Harvest Festival, and presented her with her New Year's sash, she has loved you.

GRANDMOTHER: Then, since it is so, there is some respect, too? Somewhere, deep in her heart?

MOTHER: Oh, there is. She is not a wicked child. Only headstrong and easily swayed by something new. This will pass. I pray it will pass and she will be a helpmate to her husband and win respect at the shrines of her ancestors.

GRANDMOTHER: It may pass. But not unless my generation sets an example.

FATHER: Sets an example, my mother?

GRANDMOTHER: That is what we have failed to do. We have been self-indulgent and complacent, thinking our ways safe against time and influence. We have failed to renew the old faith, have failed to sacrifice everything for our beliefs to show how greatly the heart may be swayed by duty. We have lost courage.

FATHER: My mother—

GRANDMOTHER: You know my meaning. It is the ancient, accepted way. It is the only way I know to right a wrong in the eyes of the gods and in the eyes of our watchful forbears. Otherwise, I am helpless and can make no protest except with the cawing tongue of an old woman, which no one heeds.

(She rises and moves slowly towards exit, right, as the MOTHER *and* FATHER *bow low in profound respect.)*

FATHER: We will worship at your shrine, noble Mother.

GRANDMOTHER: I thank you, my son. I will keep my watch over you. *(She bows and exits.)*

FATHER: Bring our daughter here.

(The MOTHER *bows and exits, left.)*

(The FATHER *stands, looking at the shrine intently as if trying to read the secret of life in the calm and gracious features of the timeless Buddha.*

(Enter DAUGHTER *and* MOTHER *from left. The* MOTHER *goes to the shrine, kneels before the Buddha and remains immobile during the following:)*

FATHER: *(gently)* My daughter, your hair was beautiful a few short minutes ago.

DAUGHTER: *(subdued and exhausted)* Yes.

FATHER: Do you recall, as a child, how mortified you were when the ends of your hair would curl instead of hanging straight like other little girls'?

DAUGHTER: I remember.

FATHER: Do you remember, as well, who it was who studied in old books, who made up the sticky solution, and who bought a special stiff brush with her rice-cake money? Who sat patiently hour upon hour, combing and brushing and combing again, and brushing a thousand times over, so that your hair would be straight?

DAUGHTER: It was Grandmother.

FATHER: And do you know why she did that?

DAUGHTER: To make my hair straight.

FATHER: More than that. It was to save you from shame. To set you an example of sacrifice and duty. She knew that if your hair was not straight your family would be ridiculed as well as you. And it is a woman's duty to save the honour of her family however she can. In small matters—and in great.

DAUGHTER: I can't help it if I don't think the way everyone else does.

FATHER: Honour is the same for us all.

DAUGHTER: Honour—?

FATHER: It is a word you have heard many times. Have you understood what it meant?

DAUGHTER: *(petulantly)* Oh, I don't know.

FATHER: Honour is the high reputation which we deserve, not by always being right, but by always living with respect and in accord with true principles.

DAUGHTER: How do you know when a principle is true?

FATHER: Perhaps you must look into the deeps of your heart to see how full its meaning is.

(There is a noise off, right, as of an instrument falling to the floor. The MOTHER *rises unobtrusively from the shrine and exits, centre back.)*

DAUGHTER: I believe all I have said.

FATHER: Do you believe in it strongly?

DAUGHTER: Yes, I do.

FATHER: With courage?

DAUGHTER: Yes.

FATHER: Enough to sacrifice for it?

DAUGHTER: Yes.

FATHER: Enough to sacrifice—supremely?

(The MOTHER *appears at right. She bows low.)*

MOTHER: My honoured husband, your revered mother is now with her ancestors. *(She kneels in prayer, facing the inner room, right.)*

DAUGHTER: *(staggered)* My grandmother—? My grandmother—?

FATHER: Yes.

DAUGHTER: Gone—to the other world?

FATHER: It was by her own choice and by her own hand.

DAUGHTER: Father—why? Oh, Father, why?

FATHER: Because she believed and had no other protest against your disbelief.

DAUGHTER: *(going slowly, as if hypnotized, towards exit, right)* Against—my—disbelief—?

FATHER: Yes, go in to her, so that sacrifice and honour will no longer be only words to you.

(The DAUGHTER *exits right.)*

(The FATHER *goes to the shrine and kneels before it.)*

(After a few moments the DAUGHTER *enters from right, in the extreme of her horror.)*

DAUGHTER: Mother! Mother!

(The MOTHER *does not move. The* DAUGHTER *runs across to the* FATHER.*)*

My father! My father!

(He does not move. She turns and comes down-stage.)

I believe—I believe—

(She falls down onto a cushion.)

(In a wail of anguish:)

Oh, I don't know what I believe.

(She is sobbing and beating her hands, as the Curtain falls.)

PRODUCTION

STAGE FURNISHINGS
contribute to the illusion of reality that the set designer, the carpenters and the painters have provided: the *flats* and the *backdrop*. The set designer has the final word.

1/ Against what set are the stage furnishings for "Protest" to be viewed by the audience?

2/ What basic pieces of *furniture* has the playwright specified should be on stage?
Which item has he indicated is to be given a position of importance?
How has Williams suggested that this "piece of Western furniture" is out of place in the room?

3/ Why is the audience given a few moments to examine the set and the furnishings before the action of the play begins?

STAGE PROPS
are articles the actors carry, pick up, or refer to in the course of the play.

1/ What *stage prop* is used dramatically at the very beginning of the play by the grandmother?

2/ What *props* provide the mother with the opportunity to make several entrances on stage and thereby eavesdrop on the conversation of the father and his daughter?

3/ What *prop* does the daughter carry to flaunt her newly-won independence?

4/ What *prop*, used off-stage, heightens the effect of the concluding moments of the play?

REVIEW

Suppose that a producer has chosen to run "The Ship of Dreams" and "Protest" as a double bill. Compose a review similar to one a professional drama critic might write after both plays stressing:

1/ the relative success of each playwright in illustrating the "generation gap";

2/ the focus of the conflict between the young and the old upon specific objects;

3/ the choice, in each play, of a foreign setting, although both Hughes and Williams are Canadians.

R E S E A R C H

1/ Using the resources of the reference and history sections of your school library, judge how successfully Williams has recreated the Japan of the early 1900's.

2/ Re-read the play to find at what points the reactions of the older generation to the younger are similar or different from the reactions *your* parents and grandparents would have to behaviour they did not approve of —or understand.

3/ Why might the play have been entitled, "Protests"?

R E A D I N G

1/ Copp Clark has published six of Norman Williams' plays in *Worlds Apart* (1956).

2/ Other plays which consider the gap between generations are: Bernard Shaw's *Pygmalion* and *Major Barbara* (Penguin paperbacks PL3 and PL7); Edward Albee's *The Sandbox* (Signet paperback P2339); William Gibson's *The Miracle Worker* (Bantam Pathfinder paperback FP4194); William Shakespeare's *Romeo and Juliet* and Arthur Laurent's *West Side Story* in a single paperback edited by N. Houghton (Dell LFT 7483).

THE RISING OF THE MOON LADY GREGORY

REHEARSAL

BLOCKING OUT A SCENE
involves marking, on a diagram of the stage area, where the furnishings are to be placed and where the actors will move and stand. Whether or not the director actually *sketches* such outlines for a scene or prefers to work out actors' movements in his *mind,* he gives careful consideration to both major and minor stage details at succeeding moments in the production.

1/ Imagine that the action of the play you are directing takes place at the docks of a seaport town.

Sketch the basic stage plan you would suggest to the set designer. (Place yourself above the stage, looking down.)

2/ The audience is to imagine it is looking at a dockside pier. Remembering that we are at the seaside, add details which would clearly give the members of the audience their bearings.

3/ A large barrel is to fulfil an important function in the action of the play.

Where would you place it? (Stage directions usually refer to right and left from the actor's point of view).

4/ Label the various stage furnishings on the stage plan you drew for question 1. Remember that certain details are necessary to establish the reality of the locale of the action. Will a pier and a barrel be sufficient?

5/ Three characters are to enter as the play opens. One turns out to be more important than the other two.

In what order would you have them make their entrance?

Why?

How would you indicate, by means of arrows to indicate movements and "x"s to mark stage positions, that these characters are to enter in a certain way and take up particular positions on stage?

Onto such a pier come three characters in
Lady Gregory's
"The Rising of the Moon."

The Rising of the Moon

Characters

SERGEANT

POLICEMAN X

POLICEMAN B

A RAGGED MAN

Scene: Side of a quay in a seaport town. Some posts and chains. A large barrel. Enter three POLICEMEN. *Moonlight.*

(SERGEANT, *who is older than the others, crosses the stage to right and looks down steps. The others put down a pastepot and unroll a bundle of placards.)*

POLICEMAN B: I think this would be a good place to put up a notice. *(He points to barrel.)*

POLICEMAN X: Better ask him. *(calls to* SERGEANT.*)* Will this be a good place for a placard?
(no answer)

POLICEMAN B: Will we put up a notice here on the barrel?
(no answer)

SERGEANT: There's a flight of steps here that leads to the water. This is a place that should be minded well. If he got down here, his friends might have a boat to meet him; they might send it in here from outside.

POLICEMAN B: Would the barrel be a good place to put a notice up?

SERGEANT: It might; you can put it there.
(They paste the notice up.)

SERGEANT: *(reading it)* Dark hair—dark eyes, smooth face, height, five feet five—there's not much to take hold of in that—It's a pity I had no chance of seeing him before he broke out of jail. They say he's a wonder, that it's he makes all the plans for the whole organization. There isn't another man in Ireland would have broken jail the way he did. He must have some friends among the jailers.

POLICEMAN B: A hundred pounds is little enough for the Government to offer for him. You may be sure any man in the force that takes him will get promotion.

SERGEANT: I'll mind this place myself. I wouldn't wonder at all if he came this way. He might come slipping along there *(points to side of quay)*, and his friends might be waiting for him there *(points down steps)*, and once he got away it's little chance we'd have of finding him; it's maybe under a load of kelp he'd be in a fishing boat, and not one to help a married man that wants it to the reward.

POLICEMAN X: And if we get him itself, nothing but abuse on our heads for it from the people, and maybe from our own relations.

SERGEANT: Well, we have to do our duty in the force. Haven't we the whole country depending on us to keep law and order? It's those that are down would be up and those that are up would be down, if it wasn't for us. Well, hurry on, you have plenty of other places to placard yet, and come back here then to me. You can take the lantern. Don't be too long now. It's very lonesome here with nothing but the moon.

POLICEMAN B: It's a pity we can't stop with you. The Government should have brought more police into the town, with *him* in gaol, and at assize time too. Well, good luck to your watch.

(They go out.)

SERGEANT: *(Walks up and down once or twice and looks at placard.)* A hundred pounds and promotion sure. There must be a great deal of spending in a hundred pounds. It's a pity some honest man not to be the better of that.

(A ragged man appears at left and tries to slip past. SERGEANT *suddenly turns.)*

SERGEANT: Where are you going?

MAN: I'm a poor ballad-singer, your honour. I thought to sell some of these *(holds out bundle of ballads)* to the sailors.

(He goes on.)

SERGEANT: Stop! Didn't I tell you to stop? You can't go on there.

MAN: Oh, very well. It's a hard thing to be poor. All the world's against the poor!

SERGEANT: Who are you?

MAN: You'd be as wise as myself if I told you, but I don't mind. I'm one Jimmy Walsh, a ballad-singer.

SERGEANT: Jimmy Walsh? I don't know that name.

MAN: Ah, sure they know it well enough in Ennis. Were you ever in Ennis, sergeant?

SERGEANT: What brought you here?

MAN: Sure, it's to the assizes I came, thinking I might make a few shillings here or there. It's in the one train with the judges I came.

SERGEANT: Well, if you came so far, you may as well go farther, for you'll walk out of this.

MAN: I will, I will; I'll just go on where I was going. *(goes towards steps)*

SERGEANT: Come back from those steps; no one has leave to pass down them tonight.

MAN: I'll just sit on the top of the steps till I see will some sailor buy a ballad off me that would give me my supper. They do be late going back to the ship. It's often I saw them in Cork carried down the quay in a hand-cart.

SERGEANT: Move on, I tell you. I won't have anyone lingering about the quay tonight.

MAN: Well, I'll go. It's the poor have the hard life! Maybe yourself might like one, sergeant. Here's a good sheet now. *(turns one over)* "Content and a pipe"—that's not much. "The Peeler and the goat" - you wouldn't like that. "Johnny Hart" - that's a lovely song.

SERGEANT: Move on.

MAN: Ah, wait till you hear it. *(sings)* -

There was a rich farmer's daughter lived near the town of Ross;
She courted a Highland soldier, his name was Johnny Hart;
Says the mother to her daughter, I'll go distracted mad
If you marry that Highland soldier dressed up in Highland plaid.

SERGEANT: Stop that noise.

(Man wraps up his ballads and shuffles towards the steps.)

SERGEANT: Where are you going?

MAN: Sure you told me to be going, and I am going.

SERGEANT: Don't be a fool. I didn't tell you to go that way; I told you to go back to the town.

MAN: Back in the town, is it?

SERGEANT: *(taking him by the shoulder and shoving him before him.)* Here, I'll show you the way. Be off with you. What are you stopping for?

MAN: *(who has been keeping his eye on the notice, points to it)* I think I know what you're waiting for, sergeant.

SERGEANT: What's that to you?

MAN: And I know well the man you're waiting for - I know him well - I'll be going.

(He shuffles on.)

SERGEANT: You know him? Come back here. What sort is he?

MAN: Come back is it, sergeant? Do you want to have me killed?

SERGEANT: Why do you say that?

MAN: Never mind. I'm going. I wouldn't be in your shoes if the reward was ten times as much. *(goes on off stage to left)* Not if it was ten times as much.

SERGEANT: *(rushing after him)* Come back here, come back. *(drags him back)* What sort is he? Where did you see him?

MAN: I saw him in my own place, in the County Clare. I tell you you wouldn't like to be looking at him. You'd be afraid to be in the one place with him. There isn't a weapon he doesn't know the use of, and as to strength, his muscles are as hard as that board *(slaps barrel)*.

SERGEANT: Is he as bad as that?

MAN: He is then.

SERGEANT: Do you tell me so?

MAN: There was a poor man in our place, a sergeant from Ballyvaughan - It was with a lump of stone he did it.

SERGEANT: I never heard of that.

MAN: And you wouldn't, sergeant. It's not everything that happens gets into the papers. And there was a policeman in plain-clothes, too. . . . It is in Limerick he was. . . . It was after the time of the attack on the police barrack at Kilmallock. . . . Moonlight . . . just like this . . . waterside. . . . Nothing was known for certain.

SERGEANT: Do you say so? It's a terrible county to belong to.

MAN: That's so, indeed! You might be standing there, looking out that way, thinking you saw him coming up this side of the quay *(points)*, and he might be coming up this other side *(points)*, and he'd be on you before you knew where you were.

SERGEANT: It's a whole troop of police they ought to put here to stop a man like that.

MAN: But if you'd like me to stop with you, I could be looking down this side. I could be sitting up here on this barrel.

SERGEANT: And you know him well, too?

MAN: I'd know him a mile off, sergeant.

SERGEANT: But you wouldn't want to share the reward?

MAN: Is it a poor man like me, that has to be going the roads and singing in fairs, to have the name on him that he took a reward? But you don't want me. I'll be safer in the town.

SERGEANT: Well, you can stop.

MAN: *(getting up on barrel)* All right, sergeant. I wonder, now, you're not tired out, sergeant, walking up and down the way you are.

SERGEANT: If I'm tired I'm used to it.

MAN: You might have hard work before you tonight yet. Take it easy while you can. There's plenty of room up here on the barrel, and you see farther when you're higher up.

SERGEANT: Maybe so. *(Gets up beside him on barrel, facing right. They sit back to back, looking different ways.)* You made me feel a bit queer with the way you talked.

MAN: Give me a match, sergeant *(He gives it, and man lights pipe.);* take a draw yourself? It'll quiet you. Wait now till I give you a light, but you needn't turn round. Don't take your eye off the quay for the life of you.

SERGEANT: Never fear, I won't. *(Lights pipe. They both smoke.)* Indeed it's a hard thing to be in the force, out at night and no thanks for it, for all the danger we're in. And it's little we get but abuse from the people, and no choice but to obey our orders, and never asked when a man is sent into danger, if you are a married man with a family.

MAN: *(sings)* -

As through the hills I walked to view the hills and shamrock plain,
I stood awhile where nature smiles to view the rocks and streams,
On a matron fair I fixed my eyes beneath a fertile vale,
As she sang her song it was on the wrong of poor old Granuaile.

SERGEANT: Stop that; that's no song to be singing in these times.

MAN: Ah, sergeant, I was only singing to keep my heart up. It sinks when I think of him. To think of us two sitting here, and he creeping up the quay, maybe, to get to us.

SERGEANT: Are you keeping a good lookout?

MAN: I am; and for no reward too. Amn't I the foolish man? But when I saw a man in trouble, I never could help trying to get him out of it. What's that? Did something hit me?
(rubs his heart)

SERGEANT: *(patting him on the shoulder)* You will get your reward in heaven.

MAN: I know that, I know that, sergeant, but life is precious.

SERGEANT: Well, you can sing if it gives you more courage.

MAN: *(sings)* -

Her head was bare, her hands and feet with iron bands were bound,
Her pensive strain and plaintive wail mingles with the evening gale,
And the song she sang with mournful air, I am old Granuaile.
Her lips so sweet that monarchs kissed....

SERGEANT: That's not it. . . . "Her gown she wore was stained with gore." . . . That's it - you missed that.

MAN: You're right, sergeant, so it is; I missed it. *(repeats line)* But to think of a man like you knowing a song like that.

SERGEANT: There's many a thing a man might know and might not have any wish for.

MAN: Now, I daresay, sergeant, in your youth, you used to be sitting up on a wall, the way you are sitting up on this barrel now, and the other lads beside you, and you singing "Granuaile"?...

SERGEANT: I did then.

MAN: And the "Shan Bhean Bhocht"? . . .

SERGEANT: I did then.

MAN: And the "Green on the Cape?"

SERGEANT: That was one of them.

MAN: And maybe the man you are watching for tonight used to be sitting on the wall, when he was young, and singing those same songs. . . . It's a queer world....

SERGEANT: What! . . . I think I see something coming. . . . It's only a dog.

MAN: And isn't it a queer world? . . . Maybe it's one of the boys you used to be singing with that time you will be arresting today or tomorrow, and sending into the dock....

SERGEANT: That's true indeed.

MAN: And maybe one night, after you had been singing, if the other boys had told you some plan they had, some plan to free the country, you might have joined with them . . . and maybe it is you might be in trouble now.

SERGEANT: Well, who knows but I might? I had a great spirit in those days.

MAN: It's a queer world, sergeant, and it's little any mother knows when she sees her child creeping on the floor what might happen to it before it has gone through its life, or who will be who in the end.

SERGEANT: That's a queer thought now, and a true thought. Wait now till I think it out. . . . If it wasn't for the sense I have, and for my wife and family, and for me joining the force the time I did, it might be myself now would be after breaking jail and hiding in the dark, and it might be him that's hiding in the dark and that got out of jail would be sitting up where I am on this barrel. . . . And it might be myself would be creeping up trying to make my escape from himself, and it might be himself would be keeping the law, and myself would be breaking it, and myself would be trying maybe to put a bullet in his head, or to take up a lump of a stone the way you said he did . . . no, that myself did. . . . Oh!

(gasps. after a pause) What's that? *(grasps man's arm)*

MAN: *(jumps off barrel and listens, looking out over water)* It's nothing, sergeant.

SERGEANT: I thought it might be a boat. I had a notion there might be friends of his coming about the quays with a boat.

MAN: Sergeant, I am thinking it was with the people you were, and not with the law you were, when you were a young man.

SERGEANT: Well, if I was foolish then, that time's gone.

MAN: Maybe, sergeant, it comes into your head sometimes, in spite of your belt and your tunic, that it might have been as well for you to have followed Granuaile.

SERGEANT: It's no business of yours what I think.

MAN: Maybe, sergeant, you'll be on the side of the country yet.

SERGEANT: *(gets off barrel)* Don't talk to me like that. I

have my duties and I know them. (*looks round*) That was a boat; I hear the oars.

(*goes to the steps and looks down*)

MAN: (*sings*)—

> O, then, tell me, Shawn O'Farrell,
> Where the gathering is to be.
> In the old spot by the river
> Right well known to you and me!

SERGEANT: Stop that! Stop that, I tell you!

MAN: (*sings louder*)—

> One word more, for signal token,
> Whistle up the marching tune,
> With your pike upon your shoulder
> At the Rising of the Moon.

SERGEANT: If you don't stop that, I'll arrest you.

(*A whistle from below answers, repeating the air.*)

SERGEANT: That's a signal. (*stands between him and steps*) You must not pass this way. . . . Step farther back. . . . Who are you? You are no ballad-singer.

MAN: You needn't ask who I am; that placard will tell you. (*points to placard*)

SERGEANT: You are the man I am looking for.

MAN: (*Takes off hat and wig. Sergeant seizes them.*) I am. There's a hundred pounds on my head. There is a friend of mine below in a boat. He knows a safe place to bring me to.

SERGEANT: (*looking still at hat and wig*) It's a pity! It's a pity. You deceived me. You deceived me well.

MAN: I am a friend of Granuaile. There is a hundred pounds on my head.

SERGEANT: It's a pity, it's a pity!

MAN: Will you let me pass, or must I make you let me?

SERGEANT: I am in the force. I will not let you pass.

MAN: I thought to do it with my tongue. (*puts hand in breast*) What is that?

(*voice of* POLICEMAN X *outside:*) Here, this is where we left him.

SERGEANT: It's my comrades coming.

MAN: You won't betray me . . . the friend of Granuaile.
(slips behind barrel)

(voice of POLICEMAN B:*)* That was the last of the placards.

POLICEMAN X: *(as they come in)* If he makes his escape it won't be unknown he'll make it.

*(*SERGEANT *puts hat and wig behind his back.)*

POLICEMAN B: Did any one come this way?

SERGEANT: *(after a pause)* No one.

POLICEMAN B: No one at all?

SERGEANT: No one at all.

POLICEMAN B: We had no orders to go back to the station; we can stop along with you.

SERGEANT: I don't want you. There is nothing for you to do here.

POLICEMAN B: You bade us to come back here and keep watch with you.

SERGEANT: I'd sooner be alone. Would any man come this way and you making all that talk? It is better the place to be quiet.

POLICEMAN B: Well, we'll leave you the lantern anyhow.
(hands it to him)

SERGEANT: I don't want it. Bring it with you.

POLICEMAN B: You might want it. There are clouds coming up and you have the darkness of the night before you yet. I'll leave it over here on the barrel.
(goes to barrel)

SERGEANT: Bring it with you I tell you. No more talk.

POLICEMAN B: Well, I thought it might be a comfort to you. I often think when I have it in my hand and can be flashing it about into every corner *(doing so)* that it's the same as being beside the fire at home, and the bits of bogwood blazing up now and again.
(flashes it about, now on the barrel, now on SERGEANT*)*

SERGEANT: *(furious)* Be off the two of you, yourselves and your lantern!

(They go out. MAN *comes from behind barrel. He and* SERGEANT *stand looking at one another.)*

SERGEANT: What are you waiting for?

MAN: For my hat, of course, and my wig. You wouldn't wish me to get my death of cold?

(SERGEANT *gives them.)*

MAN: *(going towards steps)* Well, good-night, comrade, and thank you. You did me a good turn tonight, and I'm obliged to you. Maybe I'll be able to do as much for you when the small rise up and the big fall down . . . when we all change places at the Rising *(waves his hand and disappears)* of the Moon.

SERGEANT: *(turning his back to audience and reading placard)* A hundred pounds reward! A hundred pounds! *(turns towards audience)* I wonder, now, am I as great a fool as I think I am?

CURTAIN

PRODUCTION

DIRECTING THE ACTORS

Actors often feel completely confident that they know exactly how to interpret a role and exactly what goes to make up a successful characterization. If this assumption were true, directors would long since have disappeared from the theatrical scene. The director, however, has one important advantage over the individual actor: he is able to see the total effect of a scene and its relationship to the production as a whole. On his visualization of everything the audience will see on stage rests the ultimate success or failure of the play.

1/ What directions would you give the three policemen at the opening of "The Rising of the Moon" to ensure that they appear to realize their relationship to the Sergeant? If this relationship is not established, why is the ending of the play unrealistic?

2/ What instructions would you give the man who turns out to be the fugitive about *his* entrance on stage? About the tone of voice in which he speaks his first lines?

3/ How could a skilled director increase the suspense of the action while the fugitive is singing the "Johnny Hart" ballad?

4/ What suggestions would you give the actor portraying the Sergeant to enable him to indicate that his attitude towards the rebel has changed from a determination to capture him, at the beginning of the play, to his decision to shield him, at the end?

REVIEW

1/ Lady Gregory appended the following note to the end of the play:

When I was a child and came with my elders to Galway for their salmon fishing in the river that rushes past the gaol, I used to look with awe at the window where men were hung, and the dark, closed gate. I used to wonder if ever a prisoner might by some means climb the high, buttressed wall and slip away in the darkness by the canal to the quays and find friends to hide him under a load of kelp in a fishing boat, as happens to my ballad-singing man. The play was considered offensive to some extreme Nationalists before it was acted, because it showed the police in too favourable a light, and a Unionist paper attacked it after it was acted because the policeman was represented "as a coward and a traitor"; but after the Belfast police strike that same paper praised its "insight into Irish character." After all these ups and downs it passes unchallenged on both sides of the Irish Sea.

Write three brief reviews of the play assuming the point of view of *each* of these people:

a) An Irish Nationalist
b) A Unionist sympathizer
c) An impartial outsider.

RESEARCH

"The Rising of the Moon" was first performed at the Abbey Theatre in Dublin, Ireland, in 1907.

1/ From a history of Ireland (or of Great Britain during the period), find out why Ireland was so divided in the opening years of the twentieth century; and when and how Eire achieved its independence.

2/ From the same source, or from literary histories of Ireland, judge the importance of the role the Abbey Theatre played in this struggle for independence.

In what countries today is the theatre used for propaganda purposes?

READING

1/ Elizabeth Coxhead has chosen and introduced *Lady Gregory: Selected Plays* (Putnam, 1962). The prominent Irish playwright, Sean O'Casey, wrote the Foreword to the book.

2/ A sampling of the work of other Irish dramatists may be found in the following paperbacks: *Five One-Act Plays*, by Sean O'Casey (St. Martin); *The Genius of the Irish Theatre*, edited by S. Barnet (New American Library Mentor MT315); *The Complete Plays of John M. Synge* (Random House Vintage paperback V178); and *Masterpieces of the Modern Irish Theatre*, edited by R. W. Corrigan (Collier-Macmillan O1219).

THE PEN OF MY AUNT GORDON DAVIOT

REHEARSAL

IMPROVISATION
is an important part of a professional actor's training. Singly, or as a member of a group, he is asked to *invent* actions and compose speeches which would follow logically from a dramatic situation with which he has been presented.

1/ Why is this sort of *training* considered valuable for an aspiring actor?

2/ The following are *situations* suggested as possible exercises in improvisation. Individually, or in groups, consider how you would *develop* these into brief improvised plays:

a) A friend, convinced of a fugitive's innocence, feels he must somehow hide him from his pursuers, and both people are sure that the house will be thoroughly searched.

b) Someone wants to conceal an especially valuable object in a place no one is likely to find it.

c) A policeman, after rudely questioning a suspect, finds that the person he has been interrogating is not only innocent, but connected with a prominent member of the community.

You have been creating improvisations from situations similar to those in which the characters in the following play are to be involved. Now see how a professional playwright tackles these same dramatic problems in Gordon Daviot's "The Pen of My Aunt."

The Pen of My Aunt

Characters

MADAME	STRANGER
SIMONE	CORPORAL

Scene: A French country house during the Occupation. The lady of the house is seated in her drawing room.

SIMONE: *(approaching)* Madame! Oh, madame! Madame, have you—

MADAME: Simone.

SIMONE: Madame, have you seen what—

MADAME: Simone!

SIMONE: But madame—

MADAME: Simone, this may be an age of barbarism, but I will have none of it inside the walls of this house.

SIMONE: But madame, there is a—there is a—

MADAME: *(silencing her)* Simone. France may be an occupied country, a ruined nation, and a conquered race, but we will keep, if you please, the usages of civilization.

SIMONE: Yes, madame.

MADAME: One thing we still possess, thank God; and that is good manners. The enemy never had it; and it is not something they can take from *us*.

SIMONE: No, madame.

MADAME: Go out of the room again. Open the door—

SIMONE: Oh, *madame*! I wanted to tell you—

MADAME: —open the door, shut it behind you—quietly—take two paces into the room, and say what you came to say. *(*SIMONE *goes hastily out, shutting the door. She reappears, shuts the door behind her, takes two paces into the room, and waits.)* Yes, Simone?

SIMONE: I expect it is too late now; they will be here.

MADAME: Who will?

SIMONE: The soldiers who were coming up the avenue.

MADAME: After the last few months I should not have thought that soldiers coming up the avenue was a remarkable fact. It is no doubt a party with a billeting order.

SIMONE: *(crossing to the window)* No, madame, it is two soldiers in one of their little cars, with a civilian between them.

MADAME: Which civilian?

SIMONE: A stranger, madame.

MADAME: A stranger? Are they soldiers from the Combatant branch?

SIMONE: No, they are those beasts of Administration. Look, they have stopped. They are getting out.

MADAME: *(at the window)* Yes, it is a stranger. Do you know him, Simone?

SIMONE: I have never set eyes on him before, madame.

MADAME: You would know if he belonged to the district?

SIMONE: Oh, madame, I know every man between here and St. Estèphe.

MADAME: *(dryly)* No doubt.

SIMONE: Oh, merciful God, they are coming up the steps.

MADAME: My good Simone, that is what the steps were put there for.

SIMONE: But they will ring the bell and I shall have to—

MADAME: And you will answer it and behave as if you had been trained by a butler and ten upper servants instead of being the charcoal-burner's daughter from over at Les Chênes. *(This is said encouragingly, not in unkindness.)* You will be very calm and correct—

SIMONE: Calm! Madame! With my inside turning over and over like a wheel at a fair!

MADAME: A good servant does not have an inside, merely an exterior. *(comforting)* Be assured, my child. You have your place here; that is more than those creatures on our doorstep have. Let that hearten you—

SIMONE: Madame! They are not going to ring. They are coming straight in.

MADAME: *(bitterly)* Yes. They have forgotten long ago what bells are for.

(Door opens.)

STRANGER: *(in a bright, confident, casual tone)* Ah, there you are, my dear aunt. I am so glad. Come in, my friend, come in. My dear aunt, this gentleman wants you to identify me.

MADAME: Identify you?

CORPORAL: We found this man wandering in the woods—

STRANGER: The corporal found it inexplicable that anyone should wander in a wood.

CORPORAL: And he had no papers on him—

STRANGER: And I rightly pointed out that if I carry all the papers one is supposed to these days, I am no good to God or man. If I put them in a hip pocket, I can't bend forward; if I put them in a front pocket, I can't bend at all.

CORPORAL: He said that he was your nephew, madame, but that did not seem to us very likely, so we brought him here.

(There is the slightest pause; just one moment of silence.)

MADAME: But of course this is my nephew.

CORPORAL: He is?

MADAME: Certainly.

CORPORAL: He lives here?

MADAME: *(assenting)* My nephew lives here.

CORPORAL: So! *(recovering)* My apologies, madame. But you will admit that appearances were against the young gentleman.

MADAME: Alas, Corporal, my nephew belongs to a generation who delight in flouting appearances. It is what they call "expressing their personality," I understand.

CORPORAL: *(with contempt)* No doubt, madame.

MADAME: Convention is anathema to them, and there is no sin like conformity. Even a collar is an offence against their liberty, and a discipline not to be borne by free necks.

CORPORAL: Ah yes, madame. A little more discipline among your nephew's generation, and we might not be occupying your country today.

STRANGER: You think it was that collar of yours that conquered my country? You flatter yourself, Corporal.

The only result of wearing a collar like that is varicose veins in the head.

MADAME: *(repressive)* Please! My dear boy. Let us not descend to personalities.

STRANGER: The matter is not personal, my good aunt, but scientific. Wearing a collar like that retards the flow of fresh blood to the head, with the most disastrous consequences to the grey matter of the brain. The hypothetical grey matter. In fact, I have a theory—

CORPORAL: Monsieur, your theories do not interest me.

STRANGER: No? You do not find speculation interesting?

CORPORAL: In this world one judges by results.

STRANGER: *(after a slight pause of reflection)* I see. The collared conqueror sits in the high places, while the collarless conquered lies about in the woods. And who comes best out of that, would you say? Tell me, Corporal, as man to man, do you never have a mad, secret desire to lie unbuttoned in a wood?

CORPORAL: I have only one desire, monsieur, and that is to see your papers.

STRANGER: *(taken off-guard and filling in time)* My papers?

MADAME: But is that necessary, Corporal? I have already told you that——

CORPORAL: I know that madame is a very good collaborator and in good standing——

MADAME: In that case——

CORPORAL: But when we begin an affair we like to finish it. I have asked to see monsieur's papers, and the matter will not be finished until I have seen them.

MADAME: You acknowledge that I am in "good standing," Corporal?

CORPORAL: So I have heard, madame.

MADAME: Then I must consider it a discourtesy on your part to demand my nephew's credentials.

CORPORAL: It is no reflection on madame. It is a matter of routine, nothing more.

STRANGER: *(murmuring)* The great god Routine.

MADAME: To ask for his papers was routine; to insist on their production is discourtesy. I shall say so to your Commanding Officer.

CORPORAL: Very good, madame. In the meantime, I shall inspect your nephew's papers.

MADAME: And what if I——

STRANGER: *(quietly)* You may as well give it up, my dear. You could as easily turn a steamroller. They have only one idea at a time. If the Corporal's heart is set on seeing my papers, he shall see them. *(moving towards the door)* I left them in the pocket of my coat.

SIMONE: *(unexpectedly, from the background)* Not in your *linen* coat?

STRANGER: *(pausing)* Yes. Why?

SIMONE: *(with apparently growing anxiety)* Your *cream* linen coat? The one you were wearing yesterday?

STRANGER: Certainly.

SIMONE: Merciful Heaven! I sent it to the laundry!

STRANGER: To the laundry!

SIMONE: Yes, monsieur; this morning; in the basket.

STRANGER: *(in incredulous anger)* You sent my coat, *with my papers in the pocket,* to the laundry!

SIMONE: *(defensive and combatant)* I didn't know monsieur's papers were in the pocket.

STRANGER: You didn't know! You didn't know that a packet of documents weighing half a ton were in the pocket. An identity card, a *laisser passer,* a food card, a drink card, an army discharge, a permission to wear civilian clothes, a permission to go farther than ten miles to the east, a permission to go more than ten miles to the west, a permission to——

SIMONE: *(breaking in with spirit)* How was I to know the coat was heavy! I picked it up with the rest of the bundle that was lying on the floor.

STRANGER: *(snapping her head off)* My coat was on the back of the chair.

SIMONE: It was on the floor.

STRANGER: On the back of the chair!

SIMONE: It was on the floor with your dirty shirt and your pyjamas, and a towel and what not. I put my arms round the whole thing and then—woof! into the basket with them.

STRANGER: I tell you that coat was on the back of the chair.

It was quite clean and was not going to the laundry for two weeks yet—if then. I hung it there myself, and——

MADAME: My dear boy, what does it matter? The damage is done now. In any case, they will find the papers when they unpack the basket, and return them tomorrow.

STRANGER: If someone doesn't steal them. There are a lot of people who would like to lay hold of a complete set of papers, believe me.

MADAME: *(reassuring)* Oh, no. Old Fleureau is the soul of honesty. You have no need to worry about them. They will be back first thing tomorrow, you shall see; and then we shall have much pleasure in sending them to the Administration Office for the Corporal's inspection. Unless, of course, the Corporal insists on your personal appearance at the office.

CORPORAL: *(cold and indignant)* I have seen monsieur. All that I want now is to see his papers.

STRANGER: You shall see them, Corporal, you shall see them. The whole half-ton of them. You may inspect them at your leisure. Provided, that is, that they come back from the laundry to which this idiot has consigned them.

MADAME: *(again reassuring)* They will come back, never fear. And you must not blame Simone. She is a good child, and does her best.

SIMONE: *(with an air of belated virtue)* I am not one to pry into pockets.

MADAME: Simone, show the Corporal out, if you please.

SIMONE: *(natural feeling overcoming her for a moment)* He knows the way out. *(recovering)* Yes, madame.

MADAME: And Corporal, try to take your duties a little less literally in future. My countrymen appreciate the spirit rather than the letter.

CORPORAL: I have my instructions, madame, and I obey them. Good day, madame. Monsieur.

(He goes, followed by SIMONE*—door closes. There is a moment of silence.)*

STRANGER: For a good collaborator, that was a remarkably quick adoption.

MADAME: Sit down, young man. I will give you something to drink. I expect your knees are none too well.

STRANGER: My knees, madame, are pure gelatine. As for my stomach, it seems to have disappeared.

MADAME: *(offering him the drink she has poured out)* This will recall it, I hope.

STRANGER: You are not drinking, madame.

MADAME: Thank you, no.

STRANGER: Not with strangers. It is certainly no time to drink with strangers. Nevertheless, I drink the health of a collaborator. *(He drinks.)* Tell me, madame, what will happen tomorrow when they find that you have no nephew?

MADAME: *(surprised)* But of course I have a nephew. I tell lies, my friend; but not *silly* lies. My charming nephew has gone to Bonneval for the day. He finds country life dull.

STRANGER: Dull? This—this heaven?

MADAME: *(dryly)* He likes to talk and here there is no audience. At Headquarters in Bonneval he finds the audience sympathetic.

STRANGER: *(understanding the implication)* Ah.

MADAME: He believes in the Brotherhood of Man—if you can credit it.

STRANGER: After the last six months?

MADAME: His mother was American, so he has half the Balkans in his blood. To say nothing of Italy, Russia, and the Levant.

STRANGER: *(half-amused)* I see.

MADAME: A silly and worthless creature, but useful.

STRANGER: Useful?

MADAME: I—borrow his cloak.

STRANGER: I see.

MADAME: Tonight I shall borrow his identity papers, and tomorrow they will go to the office in St. Estèphe.

STRANGER: But—he will have to know.

MADAME: *(placidly)* Oh, yes, he will know, of course.

STRANGER: And how will you persuade such an enthusiastic collaborator to deceive his friends?

MADAME: Oh, that is easy. He is my heir.

STRANGER: *(amused)* Ah.

MADAME: He is, also, by the mercy of God, not too unlike you, so that his photograph will not startle the Corporal too much tomorrow. Now tell me what you were doing in my wood.

STRANGER: Resting my feet—I am practically walking on my bones. And waiting for tonight.

MADAME: Where are you making for? *(as he does not answer immediately)* The coast? *(He nods.)* That is four days away—five if your feet are bad.

STRANGER: I know it.

MADAME: Have you friends on the way?

STRANGER: I have friends at the coast, who will get me a boat. But no one between here and the sea.

MADAME: *(rising)* I must consult my list of addresses. *(pausing)* What was your service?

STRANGER: Army.

MADAME: Which Regiment?

STRANGER: The 79th.

MADAME: *(after the faintest pause)* And your Colonel's name?

STRANGER: Delavault was killed in the first week, and Martin took over.

MADAME: *(going to her desk)* A "good collaborator" cannot be too careful. Now I can consult my notebook. A charming colour, is it not? A lovely shade of red.

STRANGER: Yes—but what has a red quill pen to do with your notebook?—Ah, you write with it of course—stupid of me.

MADAME: Certainly I write with it—but it is also my notebook—look—I only need a hairpin—and then—so—out of my quill pen comes my notebook—a tiny piece of paper—but enough for a list of names.

STRANGER: You mean that you keep that list on your desk? *(He sounds disapproving.)*

MADAME: Where did you expect me to keep it, young man? In my corset? Did you ever try to get something out of your corset in a hurry? What would you advise as the ideal quality in a hiding-place for a list of names?

STRANGER: That the thing should be difficult to find, of course.

MADAME: Not at all. That it should be easily destroyed in emergency. It is too big for me to swallow—I suspect they do that only in books—and we have no fires to consume it, so I had to think of some other way. I did try to memorize the list, but what I could not be sure of remembering were those that—that had to be scored off. It would be fatal to send someone to an address that—that was no longer available. So I had to keep a written record.

STRANGER: And if you neither eat it nor burn it when the moment comes, how do you get rid of it?

MADAME: I could, of course, put a match to it, but scraps of freshly-burned paper on a desk take a great deal of explaining. If I ceased to be looked on with approval my usefulness would end. It is important therefore that there should be no sign of anxiety on my part: no burned paper, no excuses to leave the room, no nods and becks and winks. I just sit here at my desk and go on with my letters. I tilt my nice big inkwell sideways for a moment and dip the pen into the deep ink at the side. The ink flows into the hollow of the quill, and all is blotted out. *(consulting the list)* Let me see. It would be good if you could rest your feet for a day or so.

STRANGER: *(ruefully)* It would.

MADAME: There is a farm just beyond the Marnay cross-roads on the way to St. Estèphe—*(She pauses to consider.)*

STRANGER: St. Estèphe is the home of the single-minded Corporal. I don't want to run into him again.

MADAME: No, that might be awkward; but that farm of the Cherfils would be ideal. A good hiding-place, and food to spare, and fine people—

STRANGER: If your nephew is so friendly with the invader, how is it that the Corporal doesn't know him by sight?

MADAME: *(absently)* The unit at St. Estèphe is a non-commissioned one.

STRANGER: Does the Brotherhood of Man exclude sergeants, then?

MADAME: Oh, definitely. Brotherhood does not really begin under field rank, I understand.

STRANGER: But the Corporal may still meet your nephew somewhere.

MADAME: That is a risk one must take. It is not a very grave one. They change the personnel every few weeks, to prevent them becoming too acclimatized. And even if he met my nephew, he is unlikely to ask for the papers of so obviously well-to-do a citizen. If you could bear to go *back* a little—

STRANGER: Not a step! It would be like—like denying God. I have got so far, against all the odds, and I am not going a yard back. Not even to rest my feet!

MADAME: I understand; but it is a pity. It is a long way to the Cherfils farm—two miles east of the Marnay crossroads it is, on a little hill.

STRANGER: I'll get there; don't worry. If not tonight then tomorrow night. I am used to sleeping in the open by now.

MADAME: I wish we could have you here, but it is too dangerous. We are liable to be billeted on at any moment, without notice. However, we can give you a good meal, and a bath. We have no coal, so it will be one of those flat-tin-saucer baths. And if you want to be very kind to Simone you might have it somewhere in the kitchen regions and so save her carrying water upstairs.

STRANGER: But of course.

MADAME: Before the war I had a staff of twelve. Now I have Simone. I dust and Simone sweeps, and between us we keep the dirt at bay. She has no manners but a great heart, the child.

STRANGER: The heart of a lion.

MADAME: Before I put this back you might memorize these: Forty Avenue Foch, in Crest, the back entrance.

STRANGER: Forty Avenue Foch, the back entrance.

MADAME: You may find it difficult to get into Crest, by the way. It is a closed area. The pot boy at the Red Lion in Mans.

STRANGER: The pot boy.

MADAME: Denis the blacksmith at Laloupe. And the next

night should take you to the sea and your friends. Are they safe in your mind?

STRANGER: Forty Avenue Foch in Crest; the pot boy at the Red Lion in Mans: and Denis the blacksmith at Laloupe. And to be careful getting into Crest.

MADAME: Good. Then I can close my notebook—or roll it up, I should say—then—it fits neatly, does it not? Now let us see about some food for you. Perhaps I could find you other clothes. Are these all you—

(The CORPORAL*'s voice is heard mingled in fury with the still more furious tones of* SIMONE. *She is yelling: "Nothing of the sort, I tell you, nothing of the sort," but no words are clearly distinguishable in the angry row.)*

(The door is flung open, and the CORPORAL *bursts in dragging a struggling* SIMONE *by the arm.)*

SIMONE: *(screaming with rage and terror)* Let me go, you foul fiend, you murdering foreign bastard, let me go *(She tries to kick him.)*

CORPORAL: *(at the same time)* Stop struggling, you lying deceitful little bit of no-good.

MADAME: Will someone explain this extraordinary—

CORPORAL: This creature——

MADAME: Take your hand from my servant's arm, Corporal. She is not going to run away.

CORPORAL: *(reacting to the voice of authority and automatically complying)* Your precious servant was overheard telling the gardener that she had never set eyes on this man.

SIMONE: I did not! Why should I say anything like that?

CORPORAL: With my own ears I heard her, my own two ears. Will you kindly explain that to me if you can.

MADAME: You speak our language very well, Corporal, but perhaps you are not so quick to understand.

CORPORAL: I understand perfectly.

MADAME: What Simone was saying to the gardener, was no doubt what she was announcing to all and sundry at the pitch of her voice this morning.

CORPORAL: *(unbelieving)* And what was that?

MADAME: That she *wished* she had never set eyes on my nephew.

CORPORAL: And why should she say that?

MADAME: My nephew, Corporal, has many charms, but tidiness is not one of them. As you may have deduced from the episode of the coat. He is apt to leave his room——

SIMONE: *(on her cue; in a burst of scornful rage)* Cigarette ends, pyjamas, towels, bedclothes, books, papers—all over the floor like a *flood.* Every morning I tidy up, and in two hours it is as if a bomb had burst in the room.

STRANGER: *(testily)* I told you already that I was sor——

SIMONE: *(interrupting)* As if I had nothing else to do in this enormous house but wait on you.

STRANGER: Haven't I said that I——

SIMONE: And when I have climbed all the way up from the kitchen with your shaving water, you let it get cold; but will you shave in cold? Oh, no! I have to bring up another——

STRANGER: I didn't ask you to climb the damned stairs, did I?

SIMONE: And do I get a word of thanks for bringing it? Do I indeed? You say: "*Must* you bring it in that hideous jug; it offends my eyes."

STRANGER: So it does offend my eyes!

MADAME: Enough, enough! We had enough of that this morning. You see, Corporal?

CORPORAL: I could have sworn——

MADAME: A natural mistake, perhaps. But I think you might have used a little more common sense in the matter. *(coldly)* And a great deal more dignity. I don't like having my servants manhandled.

CORPORAL: She refused to come.

SIMONE: Accusing me of things I never said!

MADAME: However, now that you are here again you can make yourself useful. My nephew wants to go into Crest the day after tomorrow, and that requires a special pass. Perhaps you would make one out for him.

CORPORAL: But I——

MADAME: You have a little book of permits in your pocket, haven't you?

CORPORAL: Yes. I——

MADAME: Very well. Better make it valid for two days. He is always changing his mind.

CORPORAL: But it is not for me to grant a pass.

MADAME: You sign them, don't you?

CORPORAL: Yes, but only when someone tells me to.

MADAME: Very well, if it will help you, I tell you to.

CORPORAL: I mean, permission must be granted before a pass is issued.

MADAME: And have you any doubt that a permission will be granted to my nephew?

CORPORAL: No, of course not, madame.

MADAME: Then don't be absurd, Corporal. To be absurd twice in five minutes is too often. You may use my desk—and my own special pen. Isn't it a beautiful quill, Corporal?

CORPORAL: Thank you, madame, no. *We* Germans have come a long way from the geese.

MADAME: Yes?

CORPORAL: I prefer my fountain-pen. It is a more efficient implement. *(He writes.)* For the 15th and the 16th. "Holder of identity card number"—What is the number of your identity, monsieur?

STRANGER: I have not the faintest idea.

CORPORAL: You do not know?

STRANGER: No. The only numbers I take an interest in are lottery numbers.

SIMONE: I know the number of monsieur's card.

MADAME: *(afraid that she is going to invent one)* I don't think that likely, Simone.

SIMONE: *(aware of what is in her mistress's mind, and reassuring her)* But I really *do* know, madame. It is the year I was born, with two "ones" after it. Many a time I have seen it on the outside of the card.

CORPORAL: It is good that someone knows.

SIMONE: It is—192411.

CORPORAL: 192411. *(He fills in the dates.)*

MADAME: *(as he nears the end)* Are you going back to St. Estèphe now, Corporal?

CORPORAL: Yes, madame.

MADAME: Then perhaps you will give my nephew a lift as far as the Marnay cross-roads.

CORPORAL: It is not permitted to take civilians as passengers.

STRANGER: But you took me here as a passenger.

CORPORAL: That was different.

MADAME: You mean that when you thought he was a miscreant you took him in your car, but now that you know he is my nephew you refuse?

CORPORAL: When I brought him here it was on service business.

MADAME: *(gently reasonable)* Corporal, I think you owe me something for your general lack of tact this afternoon. Would it be too much to ask you to consider my nephew a miscreant for the next hour while you drive him as far as the Marnay cross-roads?

CORPORAL: But——

MADAME: Take him to the cross-roads with you and I shall agree to forget your—your lack of efficiency. I am sure you are actually a very efficient person, and likely to be a sergeant any day now. We won't let a blunder or two stand in your way.

CORPORAL: If I am caught giving a lift to a civilian, I shall *never* be a sergeant.

MADAME: *(still gentle)* If I report on your conduct this afternoon, tomorrow you will be a private.

CORPORAL: *(after a long pause)* Is monsieur ready to come now?

STRANGER: Quite ready.

CORPORAL: You will need a coat.

MADAME: Simone, get monsieur's coat from the cupboard in the hall. And when you have seen him off, come back here.

SIMONE: Yes, madame.

(Exit SIMONE*).*

CORPORAL: Madame.

MADAME: Good day to you, Corporal.

(Exit CORPORAL*).*

STRANGER: Your talent for blackmail is remarkable.

MADAME: The place has a yellow barn. You had better

wait somewhere till evening, when the dogs are chained up.

STRANGER: I wish I had an aunt of your calibre. All mine are authorities on crochet.

MADAME: I could wish you were my nephew. Good luck, and be careful. Perhaps, one day, you will come back, and dine with me, and tell me the rest of the tale.

(The sound of a running engine comes from outside.)

STRANGER: Two years today, perhaps?

MADAME: One year today.

STRANGER: *(softly)* Who knows? *(He lifts her hand to his lips.)* Thank you, and au revoir. *(turning at the door)* Being sped on my way by the enemy is a happiness I had not anticipated. I shall never be able to repay you for that. *(He goes out.)* *(off)* Ah, my coat—thank you, Simone.

(Sound of car driving off.)

(MADAME pours out two glasses. As she finishes, SIMONE comes in, shutting the door correctly behind her and taking two paces into the room.)

SIMONE: You wanted me, madame?

MADAME: You will drink a glass of wine with me, Simone.

SIMONE: With you, madame!

MADAME: You are a good daughter of France and a good servant to me. We shall drink a toast together.

SIMONE: Yes, madame.

MADAME: *(quietly)* To Freedom.

SIMONE: *(repeating)* To Freedom. May I add a bit of my own, madame?

MADAME: Certainly.

SIMONE: *(with immense satisfaction)* And a very bad end to that Corporal!

CURTAIN

PRODUCTION

THE VISUAL ASPECTS OF A PLAY are, as we have seen, usually vital to the impact the play has on its audience. So far we have been considering each of these elements separately. Now concentrate on all the visual details involved in the production of the play you have just read.

1/ The playwright has given the

reader few instructions for the set designer. Sketch *the set* for "The Pen of My Aunt" as you imagine it would be seen by the audience.

How are you going to suggest that it is a drawing-room, that is a formal living room;

that we are in France;

and that France is at war?

2/ What suggestions would you make to the carpenters about *constructing the set* and to the painters about *colours.*

3/ How would you *costume* the four characters? Which one provides the greatest challenge for the costume designer? Why?

4/ Using either members of the class or television and movie actors, *cast* the four parts in the play?

5/ *Furnish* the drawing-room in keeping with what you think is Madame's taste (keeping in mind that it is wartime, and that a colour scheme for the walls and ceiling has already been chosen).

6/ List what *props* are necessary for the production.

To which prop would you give some prominence?

7/ At what points in the play are actors' *gestures* important? When might certain gestures emphasize a particular speech or character trait at other times in the play?

8/ Which character would be the most difficult to do *make-up* for?

9/ Are any special *lighting effects* required during the performance? Why?

REVIEW

Compose two short one-paragraph reviews:

1/ The first one to be written from the point of view of someone who had lived through the German occupation of France;

2/ The second to be written by someone who either *actually* collaborated with the Germans *or* who took part in the World War II occupation of France.

RESEARCH

A dictionary of current biography will provide you with details of the playwright's life. You may have to look her up under one of her pseudonyms, Gordon Daviot, or the other one she assumed, Josephine Tey, or under her real name, Elizabeth MacKintosh.

1/ Do any of the details of her life deepen your appreciation of "The Pen of My Aunt"? Which ones?

2/ Why do you think some writers adopt pseudonyms? What pseudonyms did the following writers adopt: Samuel Clemens, Agatha Christie, Earle Stanley Gardner, John Creasey and Mary Ann Cross?

READING

1/ Gordon Daviot's most famous full-length play, *Richard of Bordeaux* has been published in paperback by Penguin (PL31).

2/ Miss MacKintosh, writing under the pen-name of Josephine Tey, is perhaps better known as a mystery-writer. Pan paperbacks have published *Miss Pym Disposes* (G387); *Brat Farrar* (X293); *The Singing Sands* (X374); *To Love and Be Wise* (X381); *A Shilling for Candles* (X496); and *The Man in the Queue* (X559). Penguin have issued *The Daughter of Time* (990) and *The Franchise Affair* (841).

TRIFLES SUSAN GLASPELL

REHEARSAL

IMPROVISATION II

Imagine that you have been asked by a fairly well-to-do neighbour to make periodic inspections of his house while he or she is off on a pleasure cruise, and that you have agreed to do so.

1/ Create a short improvisation based on *the first visit* of the neighbour to the house. Naturally she is *curious* about what the house is like because she has never been allowed inside before.

2/ Imagine, for this improvisation, that the neighbour is not only curious but *suspicious* that something illegal has been carried on there.

3/ Suppose that, in either of these situations, the neighbour is caught in the act of snooping by her very domineering husband. How would she react, especially if she were closely examining a particular object at the time?

Both curiosity and suspicion motivate the actions of *two* women in Susan Glaspell's "Trifles."

Trifles

Characters

HENRY PETERS, *Sheriff*	LEWIS HALE
GEORGE HENDERSON, *County Attorney*	MRS. PETERS
	MRS. HALE

Scene: A gloomy kitchen in the now abandoned farmhouse of JOHN WRIGHT.

It is a gloomy room, and left without having been put in order. There are unwashed pans under the sink, a loaf of bread outside the bread-box, a dish-towel on the table and other signs of incompleted work.

The door to the outside world is in the rear wall. To the right of this, under the window, there is a sink, and to the left there is a form with a hat-rack on the wall. The fireplace is in the centre of the left wall with an armchair downstage of it and a rocking-chair upstage of it. Upstage of the fireplace there is a side-table also set against the wall. There is a kitchen table approximately in the centre of the stage with a chair at either end of it. The door leading to the other part of the house is in the wall up right. Below this, set against the wall, is a cupboard with a chair upstage and slightly to the left of it. Downstage of the cupboard is a bread-box.

As the CURTAIN *rises the outer door* C. *opens and the* SHERIFF *comes in followed by the* COUNTY ATTORNEY *and* HALE. *The* SHERIFF *and* HALE *are men in middle life, the* COUNTY ATTORNEY *is a young man. After the men there enter two women—the* SHERIFF'S *wife—she is a slight wiry woman with a thin nervous face—and* MRS. HALE. *The latter is larger and would ordinarily be called more comfortable looking, but she is disturbed now and looks fearfully about as she enters. They take up their positions* R. *to* L. *as follows: The* SHERIFF, MRS. HALE, MRS. PETERS *(the* SHERIFF'S *wife), the* COUNTY ATTORNEY *and* HALE. *The latter two are round the fire* L.

COUNTY ATTORNEY: *(rubbing his hands)* This feels good. Come up to the fire, ladies.

MRS. PETERS: *(after taking a step forward)* I'm not—cold. *(She steps* L., *then back again.)*

SHERIFF: *(unbuttoning his overcoat and stepping away from the group as if to mark the beginning of official business)* Now, Mr. Hale, before we move things about, you explain to Mr. Henderson just what you saw when you came here yesterday morning. *(He moves up to the table.)*

COUNTY ATTORNEY: (L.) By the way, has anything been moved? Are things just as you left them yesterday?

SHERIFF: *(looking about)* It's just the same. When it dropped below zero last night I thought I'd better send Frank out this morning to make a fire for us—no use getting pneumonia with a big case on, but I told him not to touch anything except the fire—and you know Frank. *(He turns away* R.*)*

COUNTY ATTORNEY: Somebody should have been left here yesterday. *(He moves to the table.)*

SHERIFF: (R.) Oh—yesterday. When I had to send Frank to Morris Centre for that man who went crazy—I want you to know I had my hands full yesterday. I knew you could get back from Omaha by today, and as long as I went over everything here myself——

COUNTY ATTORNEY: *(taking out a note book)* Well, Mr. Hale, tell just what happened when you came here yesterday morning. *(He sits* L. *of the table.)*

HALE: (L.) Well, Harry and I had started to town with a load of potatoes. We came along the road from my place and as I got here I said, "I'm going to see if I can't get John Wright to go in with me on a party telephone." I spoke to Wright about it once before and he put me off, saying folks talked too much anyway, and all he asked was peace and quiet—I guess you know about how much he talked himself; but I thought maybe if I went to the house and talked about it before his wife, though I said to Harry that I didn't know as what his wife wanted made much difference to John——

COUNTY ATTORNEY: Yes, yes; let's talk about that later, Mr. Hale. I do want to talk about that, but tell now just what happened when you got to the house.

HALE: *(taking a step* C.*)* I didn't hear or see anything; I knocked at the door, and still it was all quiet inside. I knew they must be up, it was past eight o'clock. So I knocked again, and I thought I heard somebody say, "Come in." I wasn't sure, I'm not sure yet, but I opened the door—this door *(indicating the door by which the two women are still standing)* and there in that rocker—*(pointing to it)* sat Mrs. Wright.

(They all look at the rocker.)

COUNTY ATTORNEY: What—was she doing?

HALE: She was rockin' back and forth. She had her apron in her hand and was kind of—pleating it.

COUNTY ATTORNEY: And how did she—look?

HALE: Well, she looked queer.

COUNTY ATTORNEY: How do you mean—queer?

HALE: (L.C.) Well, as if she didn't know what she was going to do next. And kind of done up.

COUNTY ATTORNEY: How did she seem to feel about your coming?

HALE: Why, I don't think she minded—one way or other. She didn't pay much attention. I said, "How do, Mrs. Wright, it's cold, ain't it?" And she said, "Is it?"—and went on kind of pleating at her apron. Well, I was surprised; she didn't ask me to come up to the fire, or to sit down, but just sat there, not even looking at me, so I said, "I want to see John." And then she—laughed. I guess you would call it a laugh. I thought of Harry and the team outside, so I said a little sharp: "Can't I see John?" "No," she says kind o' dull like. "Ain't he home?" says I. "Yes," says she, "he's home." "Then why can't I see him." I asked her, out of patience. "'Cause he's dead," says she. "*Dead?*" says I. She just nodded her head, not getting a bit excited, but rockin' back and forth. "Why—where is he?" says I, not knowing what to say. She just pointed upstairs—*(himself pointing to the room above)* like that. I got up, with the idea of going up there. I walked from there to here—then I says, "Why, what did he die of?" "He died of a rope round his neck," says she, and just went on pleatin' at her apron. Well, I went out and called Harry. I thought I might—need help. We went upstairs and there he was lyin'—with his neck——

COUNTY ATTORNEY: I think I'd rather have you go into that upstairs, where you can point it all out. Just go on now with the rest of the story.

HALE: Well, my first thought was to get that rope off. It looked . . . *(He stops, his face twitches.)* . . . but Harry, he went up to him, and said, "No, he's dead all right, and we'd better not touch anything." So we went back downstairs. She was still sitting that same way. "Has anybody been notified?" I asked. "No," says she, unconcerned. "Who did this, Mrs. Wright?" said Harry. He said it business-like—and she stopped pleatin' of her apron. "I don't know," she says. "You don't *know*?" says Harry. "No," says she. "Weren't you sleepin' in the bed with him?" says Harry. "Yes," says she, "but I was on the inside." "Somebody slipped a rope round his neck and strangled him and you *didn't wake up*?" says Harry. "I didn't wake up," she said after him. We must a' looked as if we didn't see how that could be, for after a minute she said, "I sleep sound." Harry was going to ask her more questions but I said maybe we ought to let her tell her story first to the coroner, or the sheriff, so Harry went fast as he could to River's place, where there's a telephone.

COUNTY ATTORNEY: And what did Mrs. Wright do when she knew that you had gone for the coroner?

HALE: She moved from that chair to this one over here *(pointing to a small chair in the corner)* and just sat there with her hands held together and looking down. I got a feeling that I ought to make some conversation, so I said I had come in to see if John wanted to put in a telephone, and at that she started to laugh, and then she stopped and looked at me—scared.

(The COUNTY ATTORNEY *makes a note.)*

I dunno, maybe it wasn't scared. I wouldn't like to say it was. Soon Harry got back, and then Dr. Lloyd came, and you, Mr. Peters, and so I guess that's all I know that you don't. *(He moves* L. *to the fire.)*

COUNTY ATTORNEY: *(rising and crossing below table to* R.*)* I guess we'll go upstairs first—and then out to the barn and around there. *(to the* SHERIFF*)* You're convinced that there was nothing important here— nothing that would point to any motive?

SHERIFF: Nothing here but kitchen things. *(He moves above table to* L.*)*

(The COUNTY ATTORNEY, *after again looking around the kitchen, opens the door of a cupboard* R. *and looks on a shelf. He pulls his hand away, sticky.)*

COUNTY ATTORNEY: Here's a nice mess.

(The women draw nearer.)

MRS. PETERS: *(to the other woman)* Oh, her fruit; it did freeze. *(to the* ATTORNEY*)* She worried about that when it turned so cold. She said the fire'd go out and her jars would break.

SHERIFF: (L.) Well, can you beat the woman! Held for murder and worryin' about her preserves.

COUNTY ATTORNEY: *(up* R.*)* I guess before we're through she may have something more serious than preserves to worry about.

HALE: (L.) Well, women are used to worrying over *trifles.*

(The two women move a little closer together.)

COUNTY ATTORNEY: *(with the gallantry of a young politician)* And yet, for all their worries, what would we do without the ladies? *(The women do not unbend. He goes to the sink, takes a dipperful of water from the pail and pouring it into a basin, washes his hands. He starts to wipe them on the roller towel, then turns it for a cleaner place.)* Dirty towels! *(He kicks his foot against the pans under the sink.)* Not much of a housekeeper, would you say, ladies?

MRS. HALE: *(stiffly)* There's a great deal of work to be done on a farm.

COUNTY ATTORNEY: To be sure. And yet *(with a little bow to her)* I know there are some Dickson county farmhouses which do not have such roller towels. *(He gives it a pull to expose its full length again.)*

MRS. HALE: Those towels get dirty awful quick. Men's hands aren't always as clean as they might be.

COUNTY ATTORNEY: (R.) Ah, loyal to your sex, I see. But

you and Mrs. Wright were neighbours. I suppose you were friends, too.

MRS. HALE: *(shaking her head)* I've not seen much of her of late years. I've not been in the house—it's more than a year.

COUNTY ATTORNEY: And why was that? You didn't like her?

MRS. HALE: I liked her well enough. Farmers' wives have their hands full, Mr. Henderson. And then——

COUNTY ATTORNEY: Yes——?

MRS. HALE: *(looking about)* It never seemed a very cheerful place.

COUNTY ATTORNEY: No—it's not cheerful. I shouldn't say she had the homemaking instinct.

MRS. HALE: Well, I don't know as Wright had, either.

COUNTY ATTORNEY: Oh! You mean that they didn't get on very well?

MRS. HALE: *(up* C.*)* No, I don't mean anything. But I don't think a place'd be any cheerfuller for John Wright's being in it.

COUNTY ATTORNEY: (R.C.) I'd like to talk more of that a little later. I want to get the lay of things upstairs now. *(He goes* R. *to where three steps lead to a stair door.)*

SHERIFF: *(crossing above table to* R.*)* I suppose anything Mrs. Peters does'll be all right. She was to take in some clothes for her, you know, and a few little things. We left in such a hurry yesterday.

COUNTY ATTORNEY: Yes, but I would like to see what you take, Mrs. Peters, and keep an eye out for anything that might be of use to us. Come on, Hale!

MRS. PETERS: Yes, Mr. Henderson.

(The three men exit R.*)*

(The women listen to their steps on the stairs, then look about the kitchen.)

MRS. HALE: *(up* R.C.*)* I'd hate to have men coming into my kitchen, snooping around and criticizing. *(She arranges the pans under the sink which the* ATTORNEY *had shoved out of place, and pours the dirty water into a pail.)*

MRS. PETERS: Of course it's no more than their duty.

MRS. HALE: Duty's all right, but I guess that deputy sheriff that came out to make the fire didn't make this any cleaner. *(She gives the roller towel a pull.)* Wish I'd thought of that sooner. Seems mean to talk about her for not having things slicked up when she had to come away in such a hurry.

MRS. PETERS: *(who has gone to a small table up* L. *in the corner of the room, and lifted one end of a towel that covers a pan)* She had bread set. *(She stands still.)*

(MRS. HALE *has her eyes fixed on a loaf of bread beside the bread-box, which is on a low shelf at the other side of the room.)*

MRS. HALE: *(moving slowly towards it)* She was going to put this in there. *(She picks up loaf, then abruptly drops it—then in a manner of returning to familiar things.)* It's a shame about her fruit. I wonder if it's all gone. *(She looks into the cupboard.)* I think there's some here that's all right, Mrs. Peters. Yes—here; *(holding it up)* this is cherries, too. *(looking again)* I declare I believe that's the only one. *(She gets down, bottle in her hand, and goes to the sink and wipes it on the outside.)* She'll feel awful sorry after all her hard work in the hot weather. I remember the afternoon I put up my cherries last summer.

(She puts the bottle on the big kitchen table, C., *and with a sigh, is about to sit down in the rocking-chair. Before she is seated she realizes what chair it is, and, with a slow look at it, steps back. The chair which she had touched rocks to and fro.)*

MRS. PETERS: *(crossing to* R.C.*)* Well, I must get those things from the front room closet. *(She goes to the door* R., *but after looking into the other room, steps back.)* You coming with me, Mrs. Hale? You could help me carry them.

(They go into the other room and their voices can be heard off R. *Then they reappear,* MRS. PETERS *carrying a dress and skirt,* MRS. HALE *following with a pair of shoes.)*

My, it's cold in there. *(She puts the clothes on the big table, and hurries to the fire* L.*)*

MRS. HALE: *(above table* C. *examining the skirt)* Wright

was close. *(making up a parcel)* I think maybe that's why she kept so much to herself. She didn't even belong to the Ladies' Aid. I suppose she felt she couldn't do her part, and then you don't enjoy things when you feel shabby. She used to wear pretty clothes and be lively, when she was Minnie Foster, one of the town girls singing in the choir. But that—oh, that was thirty years ago. This all you was to take in?

MRS. PETERS: She said she wanted an apron. *(She moves* C.*)* Funny thing to want, for there isn't much to get you dirty in jail, goodness knows. But I suppose just to make her feel more natural. *(crossing* R.*)* She said they was in the top drawer in this cupboard. Yes, here. And then her little shawl, that always hung behind the door. *(She opens stair door* R. *and looks.)* Yes, here it is. *(She quickly shuts the door leading upstairs.)*

MRS. HALE: *(abruptly moving towards her)* Mrs. Peters!

MRS. PETERS: (R.C.) Yes, Mrs. Hale?

MRS. HALE: (L.C.) Do you think she did it?

MRS. PETERS: *(in a frightened voice)* Oh, I don't know.

MRS. HALE: *(taking the shawl and apron from her)* Well, I don't think she did. Asking for an apron and her little shawl. Worrying about her fruit.

(The men's voices are heard off R.*)*

MRS. PETERS: *(starting to speak, then in a low voice)* Mr. Peters says it looks bad for her. Mr. Henderson is awful sarcastic in a speech and he'll make fun of her sayin' she didn't wake up.

MRS. HALE: Well, I guess John Wright didn't wake when they was slipping that rope under his neck.

MRS. PETERS: No, it's strange. It must have been done awful crafty and still. They say it was such a—funny way to kill a man, rigging it all up like that.

MRS HALE: That's just what Mr. Hale said. There was a gun in the house. He says that's what he can't understand.

MRS. PETERS: Mr. Henderson said coming out that what was needed for the case was a motive; something to show anger, or—sudden feeling.

MRS. HALE: *(who is standing by the table)* Well, I don't see any signs of anger around here. *(She puts her hand on the dish towel which lies on the table, and stands looking down at table, one half of which is clean, the other half messy.)* It's wiped to here. *(She makes a move as if to finish work, then turns and looks at loaf of bread outside the bread-box. She drops the towel. Then in that voice coming back to familiar things.)* Wonder how they are finding things upstairs. I hope she had it a little more tidy up there. *(She moves* L.*)* You know it seems kind of *sneaking*. Locking her up in town and then coming out here and trying to get her own house to turn against her!

MRS. PETERS: *(crossing* R.*)* I s'pose 'tis. *(unbuttoning her coat)* Better loosen up your things, Mrs. Peters. You won't feel them when you go out.

(MRS. PETERS *takes off her fur tippet, goes to hang it on hook at back of room* L.C., *then stands looking at the small corner table up* L.*)*

MRS. PETERS: *(moving* L.*)* She was piecing a quilt. *(She brings a large sewing-basket from the table up* L., *and puts it on the table* C., *and they look at the bright pieces.)*

MRS. HALE: It's a log cabin pattern. Pretty, isn't it? I wonder if she was goin' to quilt it or just knot it?

(Voices have been heard coming down the stairs. The SHERIFF *enters, followed by* HALE *and the* COUNTY ATTORNEY.*)*

SHERIFF: They wonder if she was going to quilt it or just knot it! *(He crosses up* C. *and opens the door.)*

(The men laugh; the women look abashed.)

COUNTY ATTORNEY: *(rubbing his hands over the fire)* Frank's fire didn't do much up there, did it? Well, let's go out to the barn and get that cleared up.

(The men exit C.*)*

MRS. HALE: *(resentfully)* I don't know as there's anything so strange, our takin' up our time with little things while we're waiting for them to get the evidence. *(She sits* R. *of the big table, smoothing out a block with decision.)* I don't see as it's anything to laugh about.

MRS. PETERS: *(apologetically)* Of course they've got awful

important things on their minds. *(She takes the chair from* L. *of table to above table and sits.)*

MRS. HALE: *(examining another block)* Mrs. Peters, look at this one. Here, this is the one she was working on, and look at the sewing! All the rest of it has been so nice and even. And look at this! It's all over the place! Why, it looks as if she didn't know what she was about!

(After she has said this they look at each other, then start to glance back at the door. After an instant MRS. HALE *has pulled at a knot and ripped the sewing.)*

MRS. PETERS: Oh, what are you doing, Mrs. Hale?

MRS. HALE: *(mildly)* Just pulling out a stitch or two that's not sewed very good. *(threading a needle)* Bad sewing always made me fidgety.

MRS. PETERS: *(nervously)* I don't think we ought to touch things.

MRS. HALE: I'll just finish up this end. *(suddenly stopping and leaning forward)* Mrs. Peters!

MRS. PETERS: Yes, Mrs. Hale?

MRS. HALE: What do you suppose she was so nervous about?

MRS. PETERS: Oh—I don't know. I don't know as she was nervous. I sometimes sew awful queer when I'm just tired.

(MRS. HALE *starts to say something, looks at* MRS. PETERS, *then goes on sewing.)*

Well, I must get these things wrapped up. They may be through sooner than we think. *(putting apron and other things together)* I wonder where I can find a piece of paper, and string. *(She rises and crosses to* R.*)*

MRS. HALE: In that cupboard, maybe.

MRS. PETERS: *(looking at the cupboard)* Why, here's a birdcage. *(She holds it up.)* Did she have a bird, Mrs. Hale? *(She moves back* C.*)*

MRS. HALE: Why, I don't know whether she did or not—I've not been here for so long. There was a man around last year selling canaries cheap, but I don't know as she took one; maybe she did. She used to sing real pretty herself.

MRS. PETERS: *(glancing around)* Seems funny to think of

a bird here. But she must have had one, or why would she have a cage? I wonder what happened to it? *(She moves up above table.)*

MRS. HALE: I s'pose maybe the cat got it.

MRS. PETERS: No, she didn't have a cat. She's got that feeling some people have about cats—being afraid of them. My cat got in her room and she was real upset and asked me to take it out.

MRS. HALE: My sister Bessie was like that. Queer, ain't it?

MRS. PETERS: *(examining the cage)* Why, look at this door. It's broke. One hinge is pulled apart.

MRS. HALE: *(also looking)* Looks as if someone must have been rough with it.

MRS. PETERS: Why, yes. *(She brings the cage forward and puts it on the table.)*

MRS. HALE: I wish if they're going to find any evidence they'd be about it. I don't like this place. *(She rises and crosses below table to the fire* L.*)*

MRS. PETERS: But I'm awful glad you came with me, Mrs. Hale. It would be lonesome for me sitting here alone. *(She sits above the table.)*

MRS. HALE: It would, wouldn't it? But I tell you what I do wish, Mrs. Peters. *(stepping* C.*)* I wish I had come over sometimes when *she* was here. I—*(looking round the room)*—wish I had.

MRS. PETERS: But of course you were awful busy, Mrs. Hale—your house and your children.

MRS. HALE: I could've come. I stayed away because it weren't cheerful, and that's why I ought to have come. *(moving* L.*, then above table to* R.) I—I never liked this place. Maybe because it's down in a hollow and you don't see the road. I dunno what it is, but it's a lonesome place and always was. I wish I had come over to see Minnie Foster sometimes. I can see now—*(She shakes her head and sits* R. *of the table.)*

MRS. PETERS: Well, you mustn't reproach yourself, Mrs. Hale. Somehow we just don't see how it is with other folks until something turns up.

MRS. HALE: Not having children makes less work—but it makes a quiet house, and Wright out to work all day, and no company when he did come in. Did you know John Wright, Mrs. Peters?

MRS. PETERS: Not to know him; I've seen him in town. They say he was a good man.

MRS. HALE: Yes—good; he didn't drink, and kept his word as well as most, I guess, and paid his debts. But he was a hard man, Mrs. Peters. Just to pass the time of day with him——. *(She shivers.)* Like a raw wind that goes to the bone. *(She pauses, her eye falling on the cage.)* I should think she would 'a' wanted a bird. But what do you suppose happened to it?

MRS. PETERS: I don't know, unless it got sick and died. *(She reaches over and swings the broken door, then swings it again. Both women watch it.)*

MRS. HALE: You weren't raised round here, were you? *(MRS. PETERS shakes her head.)* You didn't know—her?

MRS. PETERS: Not till they brought her yesterday.

MRS. HALE: She—come to think of it, she was kind of like a bird herself—real sweet and pretty, but kind of timid and—fluttery. How—she—did—change. *(She pauses; then as if struck by a happy thought and relieved to get back to everyday things.)* Tell you what, Mrs. Peters, why don't you take the quilt in with you? It might take up her mind.

MRS. PETERS: Why, I think that's a real nice idea, Mrs. Hale. There couldn't possibly be any objection to it, could there? Now, just what would I take? I wonder if her patches are in here—and her things.

(They look in the sewing basket.)

MRS. HALE: Here's some red. I expect this has got sewing things in it. *(She brings out a fancy box.)* What a pretty box. Looks like something somebody would give you. Maybe her scissors are in here. *(She opens box.)* Why——

(MRS. PETERS bends nearer, then turns her face away.)

There's something wrapped up in this piece of silk.

MRS. PETERS: Why, this isn't her scissors.

MRS. HALE: *(lifting the silk)* Oh, Mrs. Peters—it's——

(MRS. PETERS bends closer.)

MRS. PETERS: *(rising)* It's the bird.

MRS. HALE: *(jumping up)* But, Mrs. Peters—look at it! It's neck! Look at it's neck! It's all—other side to.

MRS. PETERS: Somebody wrung—its—neck.

(Their eyes meet. A look of growing comprehension, of horror. Voices are heard outside. MRS. HALE *slips box under quilt pieces, and sinks into her chair. Enter* SHERIFF *and* COUNTY ATTORNEY C.*)*

COUNTY ATTORNEY: *(as one turning from serious things to little pleasantries)* Well, ladies, have you decided whether she was going to quilt it or knot it? *(He crosses down* L.*)*

MRS. PETERS: We think she was going to—knot it. *(She reseats herself.)*

COUNTY ATTORNEY: Well, that's interesting. I'm sure. *(seeing the bird-cage)* Has the bird flown? *(He moves above table to* R.C.*)*

MRS. HALE: *(putting more quilt pieces over the box)* We think the—cat got it.

COUNTY ATTORNEY: *(preoccupied).* Is there a cat? *(He moves down* R.*)*

(MRS. HALE *glances in a quick covert way at* MRS. PETERS.*)*

MRS. PETERS: Well, not now. They're superstitious, you know. They leave.

COUNTY ATTORNEY: *(to the* SHERIFF, *continuing an interrupted conversation)* No sign at all of anyone having come from outside. Their own rope. Now let's go up again and go over it piece by piece. *(They start upstairs.)* It would have to have been someone who knew just the——

(The two women sit there not looking at one another, but as if peering into something and at the same time holding back. When they talk now it is in the manner of feeling their way over strange ground, as if afraid of what they are saying, but as if they cannot help saying it.)

MRS. HALE: She liked the bird. She was going to bury it in that pretty box.

MRS. PETERS: *(in a whisper)* When I was a girl—my kitten—there was a boy took a hatchet, and before my eyes

—and before I could get there—— *(She covers her face an instant.)* If they hadn't held me back I would have—*(She catches herself, and looks where voices are heard off* R., *then falters weakly)*—hurt him.

MRS. HALE: *(with a slow look round her)* I wonder how it would seem never to have had any children around. *(pause)* No, Wright wouldn't like the bird—*(She picks up the bird-cage)*—a thing that sang. She used to sing. He killed that, too.

MRS. PETERS: *(moving uneasily)* We don't know who killed the bird.

MRS. HALE: I knew John Wright.

MRS. PETERS: It was an awful thing was done in this house that night, Mrs. Hale. Killing a man while he slept, slipping a rope around his neck that choked the life out of him.

MRS. HALE: His neck. Choked the life out of him.

MRS. PETERS: *(with rising voice)* We don't know who killed him. We don't know.

MRS. HALE: *(her own feeling not interrupted)* If there'd been years and years of nothing, then a bird to sing to you, it would be awful—still, after the bird was still.

MRS. PETERS: *(something within her speaking)* I know what stillness is. When we homesteaded in Dakota, and my first baby died—after he was two years old, and me with no other then——

MRS. HALE: *(moving)* How soon do you suppose they'll be through looking for the evidence?

MRS. PETERS: I know what stillness is. *(pulling herself together)* The law has got to punish crime, Mrs. Hale.

MRS. HALE: *(not as if answering that)* I wish you'd seen Minnie Foster when she wore a white dress with blue ribbons and stood up there in the choir and sang. *(She rises and moves above the table, looking around the room.)* Oh, I *wish* I'd come over here once in a while! That was a crime! That was a crime! Who's going to punish that?

MRS. PETERS: *(looking upstairs)* We mustn't—take on.

MRS. HALE: I might have known she needed help! I know how things can be—for women. I tell you, it's queer, Mrs. Peters. We live close together and we live far apart. We all go through the same things—it's all just a different kind of the same thing. *(brushes her eyes, noticing the bottle of fruit, reaches out for it)* If I was you I wouldn't tell her her fruit was gone. Tell her it *ain't*. Tell her it's all right. Take this in to prove it to her. She—she may never know whether it was broke or not. *(She sits* R. *of table.)*

(MRS. PETERS *rises, takes the bottle, looks about for something to wrap it in; takes petticoat from the clothes brought from the other room, and very nerously begins winding this about the bottle.)*

MRS. PETERS: *(in a false voice)* My, it's a good thing the men couldn't hear us. Wouldn't they just laugh! Getting all stirred up over a little thing like a—dead canary. As if that could have anything to do with—with—wouldn't they *laugh*! *(She crosses to the fire and sits.)*

(The men are heard coming downstairs.)

MRS. HALE: *(under her breath)* Maybe they would—maybe they wouldn't.

COUNTY ATTORNEY: *(crossing* L. *above table)* No, Peters, it's all perfectly clear except a reason for doing it. But you know juries when it comes to women. If there was some definite thing. Something to show—something to make a story about—a thing that would connect up with this strange way of doing it——
(The women's eyes meet for an instant. Enter HALE *from outer door* C.*)*

HALE: *(up* C.*)* Well, I've got the team around. Pretty cold out there.

COUNTY ATTORNEY: *(*L.*)* I'm going to stay here a while by myself. *(to the* SHERIFF*)* You can send Frank out for me, can't you? I want to go over everything. I'm not satisfied that we can't do better.

SHERIFF: *(up* R.*)* Do you want to see what Mrs. Peters is going to take in?
(The ATTORNEY *goes to the table, picks up the apron, and laughs.)*

COUNTY ATTORNEY: Oh, I guess they're not very dangerous things the ladies have picked out. *(He moves a few things about, disturbing the quilt pieces which cover the box. He then steps back.)* No, Mrs. Peters doesn't need supervising. For that matter, a sheriff's wife is married to the law. Ever think of it that way, Mrs. Peters?

MRS. PETERS: Not—just that way.

SHERIFF: *(chuckling)* Married to the law. *(He moves towards the other room.)* I just want you to come in here a minute, George. We ought to take a look at these windows.

COUNTY ATTORNEY: *(scoffingly)* Oh, windows! *(He crosses* R. *above the table.)*

*(*MRS PETERS *rises and goes to above table* C.*)*

SHERIFF: We'll be right out. Mr. Hale.

*(*HALE *goes out* C. *The* SHERIFF *follows the* COUNTY ATTORNEY *out* R. *Then* MRS. HALE *rises, hands tight together, looking intensely at* MRS. PETERS, *whose eyes make a slow turn, finally meeting* MRS. HALE's. *A moment* MRS. HALE *holds her, then her own eyes point the way to where the box is concealed. Suddenly* MRS. PETERS *throws back the quilt pieces and tries to put the box in the bag she is carrying. It is too big. She opens the box and starts to take the bird out, but it goes to pieces and she stands there helpless. Suddenly there is a sound of voices in the other room.* MRS. HALE *snatches the box and puts it in the pocket of her big coat. The* COUNTY ATTORNEY *and* SHERIFF *enter* R.*)*

COUNTY ATTORNEY: *(down* R.*—facetiously)* Well, Henry, at least we found out that she was not going to quilt it. She was going to—what is it you call it, ladies?

MRS. HALE: *(her hand against her pocket)* We call it—knot it, Mr. Henderson.

CURTAIN

PRODUCTION

Some Final Suggestions for the Actor on Stage

SCENE STEALING
tempts the amateur actor—who is often more concerned with attracting the attention of the audience than with contributing to the success of the stage production.

1/ In what ways could an actor focus the audience's attention on himself and detract from another actor's more important speech or action?

UPSTAGING

is another unfortunate tendency of the self-centred actor. In upstaging he purposely or innocently blocks the audience's view of an actor who should at that moment be clearly visible to the whole audience.

1/ At what points in the action of "Trifles" are there opportunities offered for one actor or actress to "upstage" another?

2/ When might upstaging be *intentional,* done with the approval of the director?

CUES

Beginning actors sometimes think that learning only their own lines and perhaps *the last few words of the speeches just before their own* is sufficient.

1/ Why should every actor know as many of the other actors' lines as possible?

What would a skilled actor do if another actor either *forgets* his lines or *misses a cue?* What are such *improvisations* called?

FACING THE AUDIENCE

The audience in a conventional theatre is placed in the position of the eavesdropper, looking in on a room from which one wall has been removed.

1/ When is it imperative that an actor face the audience?

2/ Why might a director suggest that an actor turn to face instead the side of the stage—or even turn his back on the audience?

REVIEW

Compose a short review of a performance of "Trifles," comparing its dramatic impact with that of another play you have read or studied.

RESEARCH

Consult a history of the theatre for details of the following different kinds of stage and the conventions of acting that each stage demanded.

1/ The ancient Greek theatre;

2/ The medieval English "pageant wagons";

3/ The Elizabethan stage;

4/ The Stratford (Ontario) version of the Elizabethan stage.

Which of the plays in this collection would be adapted for performances on each of these stages? Which stage do you think offered the actor the greater opportunity to display his talents?

READING

1/ Susan Glaspell's "Allison's House" and "Suppressed Desires" are available in script form from Samuel French.

2/ Samuel French also publish the texts of the following mystery plays: "Shall We Join the Ladies" (James M. Barrie); "Angel Street" (Patrick Hamilton); "The Bat" (Mary Roberts Rinehart and Avery Hopwood); "The Innocents" (Henry James); "The Perfect Alibi" (A.A. Milne); "Ten Little Indians" (Agatha Christie) and "Witness for the Prosecution" (also by Miss Christie).

ORRY, WRONG NUMBER LUCILLE FLETCHER

REHEARSAL

RADIO PLAYS
in which the audience *hears* but never *sees* the actors depend for their success on the skills of certain craftsmen.

1/ Which personnel, essential to a stage production, are *unnecessary* in the production of a radio play?

2/ What *craftsmen,* besides the actor, play a more important part in the performance of a radio play? Why?

3/ How might the radio scriptwriter provide the listener with details of the *setting* of the action of the play?

4/ Why might the playwright be limited in the *number* of characters he could include in any one scene?

5/ Which of the plays you have read so far might be made into effective radio play scripts?

Lucille Fletcher's "Sorry, Wrong Number" has been called radio's most perfect script. The play was first broadcast in May of 1943—and was repeated four times in the following years. Each time the starring role was played by Agnes Moorehead. Her performance was described by *Life* magazine (September 24, 1945, pp 91-2) as "a superb example of virtuosity. . . . Getting ready for the exhausting half-hour ahead, Agnes Moorehead removes most of her jewellery, unties the collar of her dress, tests her voice, and hastily scans the script although she has committed most of it to memory. . . . The show . . . over, Agnes Moorehead slumps down. . . . On the table where she broadcasts are a half-empty water pitcher and licorice drops."

If possible, your first experience of "Sorry, Wrong Number" should be listening to Miss Moorehead's performance on Decca Record 9062. Failing that, *only* the actors reading the text of the play aloud should follow the printed text; the others should *listen* to Lucille Fletcher's "Sorry, Wrong Number."

Sorry, Wrong Number

Characters

MRS. STEVENSON	SERGEANT DUFFY
OPERATOR	THIRD OPERATOR
FIRST MAN	MAN
SECOND MAN, *George*	WESTERN UNION
CHIEF OPERATOR	INFORMATION
SECOND OPERATOR	WOMAN

SOUND: *number being dialed on phone; busy signal*

MRS. STEVENSON: *(a querulous, self-centered neurotic)* Oh —*dear! (Slams down receiver. Dials* OPERATOR.*)*

OPERATOR: Your call, please?

MRS. STEVENSON: Operator? I've been dialing Murray Hill 4-0098 now for the last three-quarters of an hour, and the line is always busy. But I don't see how it *could* be busy that long. Will you try it for me, please?

OPERATOR: Murray Hill 4-0098? One moment, please.

MRS. STEVENSON: I don't see how it could be busy all this time. It's my husband's office. He's working late to-night, and I'm all alone here in the house. My health is very poor—and I've been feeling so nervous all day—

OPERATOR: Ringing Murray Hill 4-0098.

(SOUND: *Phone buzz. It rings three times. Receiver is picked up at other end.)*

MAN: Hello.

MRS. STEVENSON: Hello? *(a little puzzled)* Hello. Is Mr. Stevenson there?

MAN: *(into phone, as though he had not heard)* Hello. *(louder)* Hello.

SECOND MAN: *(slow, heavy quality, faintly foreign accent)* Hello.

FIRST MAN: Hello. George?

GEORGE: Yes, sir.

MRS. STEVENSON: *(louder and more imperious to phone)* Hello. Who's this? What number am I calling, please?

FIRST MAN: We have heard from our client. He says the coast is clear for tonight.

GEORGE: Yes, sir.

FIRST MAN: Where are you now?

GEORGE: In a phone booth.

FIRST MAN: Okay. You know the address. At eleven o'clock the private patrolman goes around to the bar on Second Avenue for a beer. Be sure that all the lights downstairs are out. There should be only one light visible from the street. At eleven fifteen a subway train crosses the bridge. It makes a noise in case her window is open and she should scream.

MRS. STEVENSON: *(shocked)* Oh—*hello!* What number is this, please?

GEORGE: Okay. I understand.

FIRST MAN: Make it quick. As little blood as possible. Our client does not wish to make her suffer long.

GEORGE: A knife okay, sir?

FIRST MAN: Yes. A knife will be okay. And remember—remove the rings and bracelets, and the jewelry in the bureau drawer. Our client wishes it to look like simple robbery.

GEORGE: Okay, I get—

(SOUND: *a bland buzzing signal)*

MRS. STEVENSON: *(clicking phone)* Oh! *(Bland buzzing sig-*

nal continues. She hangs up.) How awful! How unspeakably—

(SOUND: *dialing. Phone buzz.)*

OPERATOR: Your call, please?

MRS. STEVENSON: *(unnerved and breathless, into phone)* Operator, I—I've just been cut off.

OPERATOR: I'm sorry, madame. What number were you calling?

MRS. STEVENSON: Why—it was supposed to be Murray Hill 4-0098, but it wasn't. Some wires must have been crossed—I was cut into a wrong number—and—I've just heard the most dreadful thing—a—a murder—and— *(imperiously)* Operator, you'll simply have to retrace that call at once.

OPERATOR: I beg your pardon, madam—I don't quite—

MRS. STEVENSON: Oh—I know it was a wrong number, and I had no business listening—but these two men—they were cold-blooded fiends—and they were going to murder somebody—some poor innocent woman—who was all alone—in a house near a bridge. And we've got to stop them—we've got to—

OPERATOR: *(patiently)* What number were you calling, madam?

MRS. STEVENSON: That doesn't matter. This was a *wrong* number. And *you* dialed it. And we've got to find out what it was—immediately!

OPERATOR: But—madam—

MRS. STEVENSON: Oh, why are you so stupid? Look, it was obviously a case of some little slip of the finger. I told you to try Murray Hill 4-0098 for me—you dialed it—but your finger must have slipped—and I was connected with some other number—and I could hear them, but they couldn't hear me. Now, I simply fail to see why you couldn't make that same mistake again—on purpose—why you couldn't *try* to dial Murray Hill 4-0098 in the same careless sort of way—

OPERATOR: *(quickly)* Murray Hill 4-0098? I will try to get it for you, madam.

MRS. STEVENSON: *(sarcastically) Thank* you.

(sound of ringing; busy signal)

OPERATOR: I am sorry. Murray Hill 4-0098 is busy.

MRS. STEVENSON: *(frantically clicking receiver)* Operator. Operator.

OPERATOR: Yes, madam.

MRS. STEVENSON: *(angrily)* You *didn't* try to get that wrong number at all. I asked explicitly. And all you did was dial correctly.

OPERATOR: I am sorry. What number were you calling?

MRS. STEVENSON: Can't you, for once, forget what number I was calling, and do something specific? Now I want to trace that call. It's my civic duty— it's *your* civic duty—to trace that call—and to apprehend those dangerous killers—and if *you* won't—

OPERATOR: I will connect you with the Chief Operator.

MRS. STEVENSON: *Please!*

(sound of ringing)

CHIEF OPERATOR: *(coolly and professionally)* This is the Chief Operator.

MRS. STEVENSON: Chief Operator? I want you to trace a call. A telephone call. Immediately. I don't know where it came from, or who was making it, but it's absolutely necessary that it be tracked down. Because it was about a murder. Yes, a terrible, cold-blooded murder of a poor innocent woman—tonight—at eleven fifteen.

CHIEF OPERATOR: I see.

MRS. STEVENSON: *(high-strung, demanding)* Can you trace it for me? Can you track down those men?

CHIEF OPERATOR: It depends, madam.

MRS. STEVENSON: Depends on what?

CHIEF OPERATOR: It depends on whether the call is still going on. If it's a live call, we can trace it on the equipment. If it's been disconnected, we can't.

MRS. STEVENSON: Disconnected?

CHIEF OPERATOR: If the parties have stopped talking to each other.

MRS. STEVENSON: Oh—but—but of course they must have stopped talking to each other by *now*. That was at least five minutes ago—and they didn't sound like the type who would make a long call.

CHIEF OPERATOR: Well, I can try tracing it. Now—what is your name, madam?

MRS. STEVENSON: Mrs. Stevenson. Mrs. Elbert Stevenson. But—listen—

CHIEF OPERATOR: *(writing it down)* And your telephone number?

MRS. STEVENSON: *(more irritated)* Plaza 4-2295. But if you go on wasting all this time—

CHIEF OPERATOR: And what is your reason for wanting this call traced?

MRS. STEVENSON: My reason? Well—for heaven's sake—isn't it obvious? I overheard two men—they're killers—they're planning to murder this woman—it's a matter for the police.

CHIEF OPERATOR: Have you told the police?

MRS. STEVENSON: No. How could I?

CHIEF OPERATOR: You're making this check into a private call purely as a private individual?

MRS. STEVENSON: Yes. But meanwhile—

CHIEF OPERATOR: Well, Mrs. Stevenson—I seriously doubt whether we could make this check for you at this time just on your say-so as a private individual. We'd have to have something more official.

MRS. STEVENSON: Oh, for heaven's sake! You mean to tell me I can't report a murder without getting tied up in all this red tape? Why, it's perfectly idiotic. All right, then. I *will* call the police. *(She slams down receiver)* Ridiculous!

(sound of dialing)

SECOND OPERATOR: Your call, please?

MRS. STEVENSON: *(very annoyed)* The Police Department—*please.*

SECOND OPERATOR: Ringing the Police Department. *(Rings twice. Phone is picked up.)*

SERGEANT DUFFY: Police Department. Precinct 43. Duffy speaking.

MRS. STEVENSON: Police Department? Oh. This is Mrs. Stevenson—Mrs. Elbert Smythe Stevenson of 53 North Sutton Place. I'm calling up to report a murder.

DUFFY: Eh?

MRS. STEVENSON: I mean—the murder hasn't been committed yet. I just overheard plans for it over the telephone . . . over a wrong number that the operator gave me. I've been trying to trace down the call myself, but everybody is so stupid—and I guess in the end you're the only people who could *do* anything.

DUFFY: *(not too impressed)* Yes, ma'am.

MRS. STEVENSON: *(trying to impress him)* It was a perfectly *definite* murder. I heard their plans distinctly. Two men were talking, and they were going to murder some woman at eleven fifteen tonight—she lived in a house near a bridge.

DUFFY: Yes, ma'am.

MRS. STEVENSON: And there was a private patrolman on the street. He was going to go around for a beer on Second Avenue. And there was some third man—a client—who was paying to have this poor woman murdered—They were going to take her rings and bracelets—and use a knife—Well, it's unnerved me dreadfully—and I'm not well—

DUFFY: I see. When was all this, ma'am?

MRS. STEVENSON: About eight minutes ago. Oh . . . *(relieved)* then you *can* do something? You *do* understand—

DUFFY: And what is your name, ma'am?

MRS. STEVENSON: *(impatiently)* Mrs. Stevenson. Mrs. Elbert Stevenson.

DUFFY: And your address?

MRS. STEVENSON: 53 North Sutton Place. *That's* near a bridge, the Queensborough Bridge, you know—and *we* have a private patrolman on *our* street—and Second Avenue—

DUFFY: And what was the number you were calling?

MRS. STEVENSON: Murray Hill 4-0098. But—that wasn't the number I overheard. I mean Murray Hill 4-0098 is my husband's office. He's working late tonight, and I was trying to reach him to ask him to come home. I'm an invalid, you know—and it's the maid's night off—and I *hate* to be alone—even though he says I'm perfectly safe as long as I have the telephone right beside my bed.

DUFFY: *(stolidly)* Well, we'll look into it, Mrs. Stevenson, and see if we can check it with the telephone company.

MRS. STEVENSON: *(getting impatient)* But the telephone company said they couldn't check the call if the parties had stopped talking. I've already taken care of *that*.

DUFFY: Oh, yes?

MRS. STEVENSON: *(high-handed)* Personally I feel you ought to do something far more immediate and drastic than just check the call. What good does checking the call do, if they've stopped talking? By the time you track it down, they'll already have committed the murder.

DUFFY: Well, we'll take care of it, lady. Don't worry.

MRS. STEVENSON: I'd say the whole thing calls for a search —a complete and thorough search of the whole city. I'm very near a bridge, and I'm not far from Second Avenue. And I know *I'd* feel a whole lot better if you sent around a radio car to *this* neighborhood at once.

DUFFY: And what makes you think the murder's going to be committed in your neighborhood, ma'am?

MRS. STEVENSON: Oh, I don't know. The coincidence is so horrible. Second Avenue—the patrolman—the bridge—

DUFFY: Second Avenue is a very long street, ma'am. And do you happen to know how many bridges there are in the city of New York alone? Not to mention Brooklyn, Staten Island, Queens, and the Bronx? And how do you know there isn't some little house out on Staten Island—on some little Second Avenue you've never heard about? How do you know they were even talking about New York at all?

MRS. STEVENSON: But I heard the call on the New York dialing system.

DUFFY: How do you know it wasn't a long-distance call you overheard? Telephones are funny things. Look, lady, why don't you look at it this way? Supposing you hadn't broken in on that telephone call? Supposing you'd got your husband the way you always do?

Would this murder have made any difference to you then?

MRS. STEVENSON: I suppose not. But it's so inhuman—so cold-blooded—

DUFFY: A lot of murders are committed in this city every day, ma'am. If we could do something to stop 'em, we would. But a clue of this kind that's so vague isn't much more use to us than no clue at all.

MRS. STEVENSON: But surely—

DUFFY: Unless, of course, you have some reason for thinking this call is phony—and that someone may be planning to murder *you?*

MRS. STEVENSON: *Me?* Oh, no, I hardly think so. I—I mean—why should anybody? I'm alone all day and night—I see nobody except my maid Eloise—she's a big two-hundred-pounder—she's too lazy to bring up my breakfast tray—and the only other person is my husband Elbert—he's crazy about me—adores me—waits on me hand and foot—he's scarcely left my side since I took sick twelve years ago—

DUFFY: Well, then, there's nothing for you to worry about, is there? And now, if you'll just leave the rest of this to us—

MRS: STEVENSON: But what will you *do*? It's so late—it's nearly eleven o'clock.

DUFFY: *(firmly)* We'll take care of it, lady.

MRS. STEVENSON: Will you broadcast it all over the city? And send out squads? And warn your radio cars to watch out—especially in suspicious neighborhoods like mine?

DUFFY: *(more firmly)* Lady, I *said* we'd take care of it. Just now I've got a couple other matters here on my desk that require my immediate—

MRS. STEVENSON: Oh! *(She slams down receiver hard.)* Idiot. *(looking at the phone nervously)* Now, why did I do that? Now he'll think I *am* a fool. Oh, why doesn't Elbert come home? *Why* doesn't he? *(sound of dialing operator)*

OPERATOR: Your call, please?

MRS. STEVENSON: Operator, for heaven's sake, will you

ring that Murray Hill 4-0098 number again? I can't think what's keeping him so long.

OPERATOR: Ringing Murray Hill 4-0098. *(rings. busy signal.)* The line is busy. Shall I—

MRS. STEVENSON: *(nastily)* I can hear it. You don't have to tell me. *(slams down receiver)* If I could only get out of this bed for a little while. If I could get a breath of fresh air—or just lean out the window—and see the street—*(The phone rings. She darts for it instantly.)* Hello. Elbert? Hello. Hello. Hello. Oh, what's the *matter* with this phone? *Hello? Hello? (slams down receiver) (The phone rings again, once. She picks it up.)* Hello? Hello—Oh, for heaven's sake, who *is* this? Hello, Hello. *Hello.*

(slams down receiver. dials operator.)

THIRD OPERATOR: Your call, please?

MRS. STEVENSON: *(very annoyed and imperious)* Hello, operator. I don't know what's the matter with this telephone tonight, but it's positively driving me crazy. I've never seen such inefficient, miserable service. Now, look. I'm an invalid, and I'm very nervous, and I'm *not* supposed to be annoyed. But if this keeps on much longer—

THIRD OPERATOR: *(a young, sweet type)* What seems to be the trouble, madam?

MRS. STEVENSON: Well, everything's wrong. The whole world could be murdered, for all you people care. And now, my phone keeps ringing—

OPERATOR: Yes, madam?

MRS. STEVENSON: Ringing and ringing and ringing every five seconds or so, and when I pick it up, there's no one there.

OPERATOR: I am sorry, madam. If you will hang up, I will test it for you.

MRS. STEVENSON: I don't want you to test it for me. I want you to put through that call—whatever it is—at once.

OPERATOR: *(gently)* I am afraid that is not possible, madam.

MRS. STEVENSON: *(storming)* Not possible? And why, may I ask?

OPERATOR: The system is automatic, madam. If someone

is trying to dial your number, there is no way to check whether the call is coming through the system or not—unless the person who is trying to reach you complains to his particular operator—

MRS. STEVENSON: Well, of all the stupid, complicated—! And meanwhile *I've* got to sit here in my bed, *suffering* every time that phone rings, imagining everything—

OPERATOR: I will try to check it for you, madam.

MRS. STEVENSON: Check it! Check it! That's all anybody can do. Of all the stupid, idiotic . . . ! *(She hangs up.)* Oh—what's the use . . . *(Instantly* MRS. STEVENSON'S *phone rings again. She picks up the receiver. wildly.)* Hello. HELLO. Stop ringing, do you hear me? Answer me? What do you want? Do you realize you're driving me crazy? Stark, staring—

MAN: *(dull, flat voice)* Hello. Is this Plaza 4-2295?

MRS. STEVENSON: *(catching her breath)* Yes. Yes. This is Plaza 4-2295.

MAN: This is Western Union. I have a telegram here for Mrs. Elbert Stevenson. Is there anyone to receive the message?

MRS. STEVENSON: *(trying to calm herself)* I am Mrs. Stevenson.

WESTERN UNION: *(reading flatly)* The telegram is as follows: "Mrs. Elbert Stevenson. 53 North Sutton Place, New York, New York. Darling. Terribly sorry. Tried to get you for last hour, but line busy. Leaving for Boston 11 P.M. tonight on urgent business. Back tomorrow afternoon. Keep happy. Love. Signed. Elbert."

MRS. STEVENSON: *(breathlessly, aghast, to herself)* Oh—no—

WESTERN UNION: That is all, madam. Do you wish us to deliver a copy of the message?

MRS. STEVENSON: No—no, thank you.

WESTERN UNION: Thank you, madam. Good night. *(He hangs up phone.)*

MRS. STEVENSON: *(mechanically, to phone)* Good night. *(She hangs up slowly, suddenly bursting into tears.)* No—no—it isn't true! He couldn't do it. Not when he knows I'll be all alone. It's some trick—some fiendish— *(She dials operator.)*

OPERATOR: *(coolly)* Your call, please?

MRS. STEVENSON: Operator—try that Murray Hill 4-0098 number for me just once more, please.

OPERATOR: Ringing Murray Hill 4-0098. *(Call goes through. We hear ringing at other end. Ring after ring.)*

MRS. STEVENSON: He's gone. Oh, Elbert, how could you? How could you—? *(She hangs up phone, sobbing pityingly to herself, turning restlessly.)* But I can't be alone tonight. I can't. If I'm alone one more second—I don't care what he says—or what the expense is—I'm a sick woman—I'm entitled— *(She dials* INFORMATION.)

INFORMATION: This is Information.

MRS. STEVENSON: I want the telephone number of Henchley Hospital.

INFORMATION: Henchley Hospital? Do you have the address, madam?

MRS. STEVENSON: No. It's somewhere in the seventies, though. It's a very small, private, and exclusive hospital where I had my appendix out two years ago. Henchley. *H-E-N-C—*

INFORMATION: One moment, please.

MRS. STEVENSON: Please—hurry. And please—what *is* the time?

INFORMATION: I do not know, madam. You may find out the time by dialing Meridian 7-1212.

MRS. STEVENSON: *(irritated)* Oh, for heaven's sake! Couldn't you—?

INFORMATION: The number of Henchley Hospital is Butterfield 7-0105, madam.

MRS STEVENSON: Butterfield 7-0105. *(She hangs up before she finishes speaking, and immediately dials number as she repeats it.)*

(Phone rings.)

WOMAN: *(middle-aged, solid, firm, practical)* Henchley Hospital, good evening.

MRS. STEVENSON: Nurses' Registry.

WOMAN: Who was it you wished to speak to, please?

MRS. STEVENSON: *(high-handed)* I want the Nurses' Registry at once. I want a trained nurse. I want to hire her immediately. For the night.

WOMAN: I see. And what is the nature of the case, madam?

MRS. STEVENSON: Nerves. I'm very nervous. I need soothing—and companionship. My husband is away—and I'm—

WOMAN: Have you been recommended to us by any doctor in particular, madam?

MRS. STEVENSON: No. But I really don't see why all this catechizing is necessary. I want a trained nurse. I was a patient in your hospital two years ago. And after all, I *do* expect to *pay* this person—

WOMAN: We quite understand that, madam. But registered nurses are very scarce just now—and our superintendent has asked us to send people out only on cases where the physician in charge feels it is absolutely necessary.

MRS. STEVENSON: *(growing hysterical)* Well, it *is* absolutely necessary. I'm a sick woman. I—I'm very upset. Very. I'm alone in this house—and I'm an invalid —and tonight I overheard a telephone conversation that upset me dreadfully. About a murder—a poor woman who was going to be murdered at eleven fifteen—tonight in fact, if someone doesn't come at once—I'm afraid I'll go out of my mind—*(almost off handle by now).*

WOMAN: *(calmly)* I see. Well, I'll speak to Miss Phillips as soon as she comes in. And what is your name, madam?

MRS. STEVENSON: Miss Phillips. And when do you expect her in?

WOMAN: I really don't know, madam. She went out to supper at eleven o'clock.

MRS. STEVENSON: Eleven o'clock. But it's not eleven yet. *(She cries out.)* Oh, my clock *has* stopped. I thought it was running down. What time is it?

WOMAN: Just fourteen minutes past eleven.

(Sound of phone receiver being lifted on same line as MRS. STEVENSON'S. *A click.)*

MRS. STEVENSON: *(crying out)* What's *that*?

WOMAN: What was what, madam?

MRS. STEVENSON: That—that click just now—in my own telephone? As though someone had lifted the receiver off the hook of the extension phone downstairs—

WOMAN: I didn't hear it, madam. Now—about this—

MRS. STEVENSON: *(scared)* But I *did.* There's someone in this house. Someone downstairs in the kitchen. And they're listening to me now. They're—*(Hangs up phone. In a suffocated voice.)* I won't pick it up. I won't let them hear me. I'll be quiet—and they'll think—*(with growing terror)* But if I don't call someone now—while they're still down there—there'll be no time. *(She picks up receiver. Bland buzzing signal. She dials operator. Ring twice.)*

OPERATOR: *(fat and lethargic)* Your call, please?

MRS. STEVENSON: *(a desperate whisper)* Operator, I—I'm in desperate trouble—I—

OPERATOR: I cannot hear you, madam. Please speak louder.

MRS. STEVENSON: *(still whispering)* I don't dare. I—there's someone listening. Can you hear me now?

OPERATOR: Your call, please? What number are you calling, madam?

MRS. STEVENSON: *(desperately)* You've got to hear me. Oh, please. You've got to help me. There's someone in this house. Someone who's going to murder me. And you've got to get in touch with the—*(click of receiver being put down in* MRS. STEVENSON'S *line. bursting out wildly.)* Oh, there it is—he's put it down—he's put down the extension—he's coming—*(She screams.)* He's coming up the stairs—*(hoarsely)* Give me the Police Department— *(screaming)* The police!

OPERATOR: Ringing the Police Department.

(Phone is rung. We hear sound of a train beginning to fade in. On second ring, MRS. STEVENSON *screams again, but roaring of train drowns out her voice. For a few seconds we hear nothing but roaring of train, then dying away, phone at police headquarters ringing.)*

DUFFY: Police Department. Precinct 43. Duffy speaking. *(pause)* Police Department. Duffy speaking.

GEORGE: Sorry. Wrong number. *(hangs up)*

FADE OUT

PRODUCTION

Tape a performance of "Sorry, Wrong Number." Sound effects records are available (listed in the *Schwan Catalogue* available at major record stores), but try to improvise your own sound effects. When the taping is finished, play it to the class, accept their comments and re-tape the parts of the play which do not effectively communicate to the *listening* audience.

RESEARCH

1/ What radio plays are carried on the CBC? Do any of the American radio stations you listen to—or any of the privately-owned Canadian radio stations—schedule regular drama series, or even single radio plays? Why?

2/ What role does "talk" play in private radio station programming? What kind of "talk-show" is most popular with teen-agers? With adults?

REVIEW

Imagine that Miss Moorehead, more than twenty-five years after her first performance, stars in a radio revival of "Sorry, Wrong Number." Compose the review you think a modern radio critic would write.

READING

Some idea of the popularity of radio drama can be gleaned from M.M. Nagelberg's edition of *Drama in Our Time* (Harcourt, Brace and World—Longmans, 1948).

VISIT TO A SMALL PLANET GORE VIDAL

REHEARSAL

TELEVISION PLAYS
like movies, offer unique opportunities for audience involvement.

1/ Although the actors may move about in a stage production, how is the audience's *point of view* restricted?

2/ What *technicians* assume vital roles in the production of television plays and movies? How in these media is the director able to control the audience's point of view?

3/ What added *dimension* does the "close-up" shot offer the television or movie director? How can the theatregoer obtain somewhat the same close-up view of the action of a stage play?

4/ Live radio drama gave way to taped and recorded performances, and television plays soon came to be videotaped. What advantages does the pre-recorded, as opposed to the live, performance have for the actors? For the director?

5/ Why was the original version of "Sorry, Wrong Number" 25 rather than 30 minutes long?

6/ How do the *commercials* influence the television playwright in constructing his play?

Is the effect created by *contrasting* the world the playwright has created with the short dramas the advertisers insert good or bad? Why?

7/ How much time is alloted for commercials in each half-hour television play? Are you sufficiently annoyed by the commercials to subscribe to a private cable company's television broadcasts which you— rather than the advertisers— pay for?

Why?

One of television's more successful plays (later transferred to the Broadway stage) was Gore Vidal's "Visit to a Small Planet."

Visit to a Small Planet

Characters

KRETON	GENERAL POWERS
ROGER SPELDING	AIDE
ELLEN SPELDING	PAUL LAURENT
MRS. SPELDING	SECOND VISITOR
TWO TECHNICIANS	PRESIDENT OF PARAGUAY
JOHN RANDOLPH	

ACT ONE

Stock Shot: The night sky, stars. Then slowly a luminous object arcs into view. As it is almost upon us, dissolve to the living room of the Spelding house in Maryland.

Superimpose card: "The Time: The Day After Tomorrow"

The room is comfortably balanced between the expensively decorated and the homely. ROGER SPELDING *is concluding his TV broadcast. He is middle-aged, unctuous, resonant. His wife, bored and vague, knits passively while he talks at his desk. Two technicians are on hand, operating the equipment. His daughter,* ELLEN, *a lively girl of twenty, fidgets as she listens.*

SPELDING: *(into microphone)* . . . and so, according to General Powers . . . who should know if anyone does

. . . the flying object which has given rise to so much irresponsible conjecture is nothing more than a meteor passing through the earth's orbit. It is not, as many believe, a secret weapon of this country. Nor is it a space ship as certain lunatic elements have suggested. General Powers has assured me that it is highly doubtful there is any form of life on other planets capable of building a space ship. "If any traveling is to be done in space, we will do it first." And those are his exact words. . . . Which winds up another week of news. *(crosses to pose with wife and daughter)* This is Roger Spelding, saying good night to Mother and Father America, from my old homestead in Silver Glen, Maryland, close to the warm pulse-beat of the nation.

TECHNICIAN: Good show tonight, Mr. Spelding.

SPELDING: Thank you.

TECHNICIAN: Yes sir, you were right on time.

*(*SPELDING *nods wearily, his mechanical smile and heartiness suddenly gone.)*

MRS. SPELDING: Very nice, dear. Very nice.

TECHNICIAN: See you next week, Mr. Spelding.

SPELDING: Thank you, boys.

(Technicians go.)

SPELDING: Did you like the broadcast, Ellen?

ELLEN: Of course I did, Daddy.

SPELDING: Then what did I say?

ELLEN: Oh, that's not fair.

SPELDING: It's not very flattering when one's own daughter won't listen to what one says while millions of people. . . .

ELLEN: I always listen, Daddy, you know that.

MRS. SPELDING: We love your broadcasts, dear. I don't know what we'd do without them.

SPELDING: Starve.

ELLEN: I wonder what's keeping John?

SPELDING: Certainly not work.

ELLEN: Oh, Daddy, stop it! John works very hard and you know it.

MRS. SPELDING: Yes, he's a perfectly nice boy, Roger. I like him.

SPELDING: I know. I know: he has every virtue except the most important one: he has no get-up-and-go.

ELLEN: *(precisely)* He doesn't want to get up and he doesn't want to go because he's already where he wants to be on his own farm which is exactly where *I'm* going to be when we're married.

SPELDING: More thankless than a serpent's tooth is an ungrateful child.

ELLEN: I don't think that's right. Isn't it "more deadly. . . ."

SPELDING: Whatever the exact quotation is, I stand by the sentiment.

MRS. SPELDING: Please don't quarrel. It always gives me a headache.

SPELDING: I never quarrel. I merely reason, in my simple way, with Miss Know-it-all here.

ELLEN: Oh, Daddy! Next you'll tell me I should marry for money.

SPELDING: There is nothing wrong with marrying a wealthy man. The horror of it has always eluded me. However, my only wish is that you marry someone hard-working, ambitious, a man who'll make his mark in the world. Not a boy who plans to sit on a farm all his life growing peanuts.

ELLEN: English walnuts.

SPELDING: Will you stop correcting me?

ELLEN: But, Daddy, John grows walnuts. . . .

*(*JOHN *enters, breathlessly.)*

JOHN: Come out! Quickly. It's coming this way. It's going to land right here!

SPELDING: *What's* going to land?

JOHN: The space ship. Look!

SPELDING: Apparently you didn't hear my broadcast. The flying object in question is a meteor, not a space ship. *(*JOHN *has gone out with* ELLEN. SPELDING *and* MRS. SPELDING *follow.)*

MRS. SPELDING: Oh, my! Look! Something *is* falling! Roger, you don't think it's going to hit the house, do you?

SPELDING: The odds against being hit by a falling object

that size are, I should say, roughly, ten million to one.

JOHN: Ten million to one or not it's going to land right here and it's *not* falling.

SPELDING: I'm sure it's a meteor.

MRS. SPELDING: Shouldn't we go down to the cellar?

SPELDING: If it's not a meteor, it's an optical illusion . . . mass hysteria.

ELLEN: Daddy, it's a real space ship. I'm sure it is.

SPELDING: Or maybe a weather balloon. Yes, that's what it is. General Powers said only yesterday. . . .

JOHN: It's landing!

SPELDING: I'm going to call the police . . . the army! *(bolts inside)*

ELLEN: Oh look how it shines!

JOHN: Here it comes!

MRS. SPELDING: Right in my rose garden!

ELLEN: Maybe it's a balloon.

JOHN: No, it's a space ship and right in your own backyard.

ELLEN: What makes it shine so?

JOHN: I don't know but I'm going to find out. *(runs off toward the light)*

ELLEN: Oh, darling, don't! John, please! John, John come back!

*(*SPELDING*, wide-eyed, returns.)*

MRS. SPELDING: Roger, it's landed right in my rose garden.

SPELDING: I got General Powers. He's coming over. He said they've been watching this thing. They . . . they don't know what it is.

ELLEN: You mean it's nothing of ours?

SPELDING: They believe it . . . *(swallows hard)* . . . it's from outer space.

ELLEN: And John's down there! Daddy, get a gun or something.

SPELDING: Perhaps we'd better leave the house until the army gets here.

ELLEN: We can't leave John.

SPELDING: I can. *(peers nearsightedly)* Why, it's not much larger than a car. I'm sure it's some kind of meteor.

ELLEN: Meteors are blazing hot.

SPELDING: This is a cold one. . . .

ELLEN: It's opening . . . the whole side's opening! *(shouts)* John! Come back! Quick. . . .

MRS. SPELDING: Why, there's a man getting out of it! *(sighs)* I feel much better already. I'm sure if we ask him, he'll move that thing for us. Roger, you ask him.

SPELDING: *(ominously)* If it's really a man?

ELLEN: John's shaking hands with him. *(calls)* John darling, come on up here. . . .

MRS. SPELDING: And bring your friend. . . .

SPELDING: There's something wrong with the way that creature looks . . . if it is a man and not a . . . not a monster.

MRS. SPELDING: He looks perfectly nice to me.

(JOHN and the VISITOR appear. The VISITOR is in his forties, a mild, pleasant-looking man with side-whiskers and dressed in the fashion of 1860. He pauses when he sees the three people, in silence for a moment. They stare back at him, equally interested.)

VISITOR: I seem to've made a mistake. I *am* sorry. I'd better go back and start over again.

SPELDING: My dear sir, you've only just arrived. Come in, come in. I don't need to tell you what a pleasure this is . . . Mister . . . Mister. . . .

VISITOR: Kreton. . . . This *is* the wrong costume, isn't it?

SPELDING: Wrong for what?

KRETON: For the country, and the time.

SPELDING: Well, it's a trifle old-fashioned.

MRS. SPELDING: But really awfully handsome.

KRETON: Thank you.

MRS. SPELDING: *(to husband)* Ask him about moving that thing off my rose bed.

(SPELDING leads them all into living room.)

SPELDING: Come on in and sit down. You must be tired after your trip.

KRETON: Yes, I am a little. *(looks around delightedly)* Oh, it's better than I'd hoped!

SPELDING: Better? What's better?

KRETON: The house . . . that's what you call it? Or is this an apartment?

SPELDING: This is a house in the State of Maryland, U.S.A.

KRETON: In the late 20th century! To think this is really

the 20th century. I must sit down a moment and collect myself. The *real* thing! *(He sits down.)*

ELLEN: You . . . you're not an American, are you?

KRETON: What a nice thought! No, I'm not.

JOHN: You sound more English.

KRETON: Do I? Is my accent very bad?

JOHN: No, it's quite good.

SPELDING: Where *are* you from, Mr. Kreton?

KRETON: *(evasively)* Another place.

SPELDING: On this earth of course.

KRETON: No, not on this planet.

ELLEN: Are you from Mars?

KRETON: Oh dear no, not Mars. There's nobody on Mars . . . at least no one I know.

ELLEN: I'm sure you're testing us and this is all some kind of publicity stunt.

KRETON: No, I really am from another place.

SPELDING: I don't suppose you'd consent to my interviewing you on television?

KRETON: I don't think your authorities will like that. They are terribly upset as it is.

SPELDING: How do you know?

KRETON: Well, I . . . pick up things. For instance, I know that in a few minutes a number of people from your Army will be here to question me and they . . . like you . . . are torn by doubt.

SPELDING: How extraordinary!

ELLEN: Why did you come here?

KRETON: Simply a visit to your small planet. I've been studying it for years. In fact, one might say, you people are my hobby. Especially, this period of your development.

JOHN: Are you the first person from your . . . your planet to travel in space like this?

KRETON: Oh my no! Everyone travels who wants to. It's just that no one wants to visit you. I can't think why. *I* always have. You'd be surprised what a thorough study I've made. *(recites)* The planet, Earth, is divided into five continents with a number of large islands. It is mostly water. There is one moon. Civilization is only just beginning. . . .

SPELDING: Just beginning! My dear sir, we have had. . . .

KRETON: *(blandly)* You are only in the initial stages, the most fascinating stage as far as I'm concerned. . . . I do hope I don't sound patronizing.

ELLEN: Well, we are very proud.

KRETON: I know and that's one of your most endearing, primitive traits. Oh, I can't believe I'm here at last!

*(*GENERAL POWERS, *a vigorous product of the National Guard, and his* AIDE *enter.)*

POWERS: All right folks. The place is surrounded by troops. Where is the monster?

KRETON: I, my dear General, am the monster.

POWERS: What are you dressed up for, a fancy-dress party?

KRETON: I'd hoped to be in the costume of the period. As you see I am about a hundred years too late.

POWERS: Roger, who is this joker?

SPELDING: This is Mr. Kreton . . . General Powers. Mr. Kreton arrived in that thing outside. He is from another planet.

POWERS: I don't believe it.

ELLEN: It's true. We saw him get out of the flying saucer.

POWERS: *(to* AIDE*)* Captain, go down and look at that ship. But be careful. Don't touch anything. And don't let anybody else near it. *(*AIDE *goes.)* So you're from another planet.

KRETON: Yes. My, that's a very smart uniform but I prefer the ones made of metal, the ones you used to wear, you know: with the feathers on top.

POWERS: That was five hundred years ago. . . . Are you *sure* you're not from the Earth?

KRETON: Yes.

POWERS Well, I'm not. You've got some pretty tall explaining to do.

KRETON: Anything to oblige.

POWERS All right, which planet?

KRETON: None that you have ever heard of.

POWERS: Where is it?

KRETON: You wouldn't know.

POWERS: This solar system?

KRETON: No.

POWERS: Another system?

KRETON: Yes.

POWERS: Look, Buster, I don't want to play games: I just want to know where you're from. The law requires it.

KRETON: It's possible that I could explain it to a mathematician but I'm afraid I couldn't explain it to you, not for another five hundred years and by then of course *you'd* be dead because you people do die, don't you?

POWERS: What?

KRETON: Poor fragile butterflies, such brief little moments in the sun. . . . You see *we* don't die.

POWERS: You'll die all right if it turns out you're a spy or a hostile alien.

KRETON: I'm sure you wouldn't be so cruel.

(AIDE returns; he looks disturbed.)

POWERS: What did you find?

AIDE: I'm not sure, General.

POWERS: *(heavily)* Then do your best to describe what the object is like.

AIDE: Well, it's elliptical, with a fourteen-foot diameter. And it's made of an unknown metal which shines and inside there isn't anything.

POWERS: Isn't anything?

AIDE: There's nothing inside the ship: No instruments, no food, nothing.

POWERS: *(to KRETON)* What did you do with your instrument board?

KRETON: With my what? Oh, I don't have one.

POWERS: How does the thing travel?

KRETON: I don't know.

POWERS: You don't know. Now look, Mister, you're in pretty serious trouble. I suggest you do a bit of cooperating. You claim you traveled here from outer space in a machine with no instruments. . . .

KRETON: Well, these cars are rather common in my world and I suppose, once upon a time, I must've known the theory on which they operate but I've long since forgotten. After all, General, we're not mechanics, you and I.

POWERS: Roger, do you mind if we use your study?

SPELDING: Not at all. Not at all, General.

POWERS: Mr. Kreton and I are going to have a chat. *(to* AIDE*)* Put in a call to the Chief of Staff.

AIDE: Yes, General.

*(*SPELDING *rises, leads* KRETON *and* POWERS *into next room, a handsomely furnished study, many books and a globe of the world.)*

SPELDING: This way, gentlemen.

*(*KRETON *sits down comfortably beside the globe which he twirls thoughtfully. At the door,* SPELDING *speaks in a low voice to* POWERS.*)*

I hope I'll be the one to get the story first, Tom.

POWERS: There isn't any story. Complete censorship. I'm sorry but this house is under martial law. I've a hunch we're in trouble.

(He shuts the door. SPELDING *turns and rejoins his family.)*

ELLEN: I think he's wonderful, whoever he is.

MRS. SPELDING: I wonder how much damage he did to my rose garden. . . .

JOHN: It's sure hard to believe he's really from outer space. No instruments, no nothing . . . boy, they must be advanced scientifically.

MRS. SPELDING: Is he spending the night, dear?

SPELDING: What?

MRS. SPELDING: Is he spending the night?

SPELDING: Oh, yes, yes, I suppose he will be.

MRS. SPELDING: Then I'd better go make up the bedroom. He seems perfectly nice to me. I like his whiskers. They're so very . . . comforting. Like Grandfather Spelding's. *(She goes.)*

SPELDING: *(bitterly)* I *know* this story will leak out before I can interview him. I just know it.

ELLEN: What does it mean, we're under martial law?

SPELDING: It means we have to do what General Powers tells us to do. *(He goes to the window as a soldier passes by.)* See?

JOHN: I wish I'd taken a closer look at that ship when I had the chance.

ELLEN: Perhaps he'll give us a ride in it.

JOHN: Traveling in space! Just like those stories. You know: intergalactic drive stuff.

SPELDING: *If* he's not an imposter.

ELLEN: I have a feeling he isn't.

JOHN: Well, I better call the family and tell them I'm all right.

(He crosses to telephone by the door which leads into hall.)

AIDE: I'm sorry, sir, but you can't use the phone.

SPELDING: He certainly can. This is my house. . . .

AIDE: *(mechanically)* This house is a military reservation until the crisis is over: Order General Powers. I'm sorry.

JOHN: How am I to call home to say where I am?

AIDE: Only General Powers can help you. You're also forbidden to leave this house without permission.

SPELDING: You can't do this!

AIDE: I'm afraid, sir, we've done it.

ELLEN: Isn't it exciting!

(cut to study)

POWERS: Are you deliberately trying to confuse me?

KRETON: Not deliberately, no.

POWERS: We have gone over and over this for two hours now and all that you've told me is that you're from another planet in another solar system. . . .

KRETON: In another dimension. I think that's the word you use.

POWERS: In another dimension and you have come here as a tourist.

KRETON: Up to a point, yes. What did you expect?

POWERS: It is my job to guard the security of this country.

KRETON: I'm sure that must be very interesting work.

POWERS: For all I know, you are a spy, sent here by an alien race to study us, preparatory to invasion.

KRETON: Oh, none of my people would *dream* of invading you.

POWERS: How do I know that's true?

KRETON: You don't, so I suggest you believe me. I should also warn you: I can tell what's inside.

POWERS: What's inside?

KRETON: What's inside your mind.

POWERS: You're a mind reader?

KRETON: I don't really read it. I hear it.

POWERS: What am I thinking?

KRETON: That I am either a lunatic from the earth or a spy from another world.

POWERS: Correct. But then you could've guessed that. *(frowns)* What am I thinking now?

KRETON: You're making a picture. Three silver stars. you're pinning them on your shoulder, instead of the two stars you now wear.

POWERS: *(startled)* That's right. I was thinking of my promotion.

KRETON: If there's anything I can do to hurry it along, just let me know.

POWERS: You can. Tell me why you're here.

KRETON: Well, we don't travel much, my people. We used to but since we see everything through special monitors and recreators, there is no particular need to travel. However, *I* am a hobbyist. I love to gad about.

POWERS: *(taking notes)* Are you the first to visit us?

KRETON: Oh, no! We started visiting you long before there were people on the planet. However, we are seldom noticed on our trips. I'm sorry to say I slipped up, coming in the way I did . . . but then this visit was all rather impromptu. *(laughs)* I am a creature of impulse, I fear.

(AIDE looks in.)

AIDE: Chief of Staff on the telephone, General.

POWERS: *(picks up phone)* Hello, yes, sir. Powers speaking. I'm talking to him now. No, sir. No, sir. No, we can't determine what method of power was used. He won't talk. Yes, sir. I'll hold him there. I've put the house under martial law . . . belongs to a friend of mine, Roger Spelding, the TV commentator. Roger Spelding, the TV. . . . What? Oh, no, I'm sure he won't say anything. Who . . . oh, yes, sir. Yes, I realize the importance of it. Yes, I will. Good-by. *(hangs up)* The President of the United States wants to know all about you.

KRETON: How nice of him! And I want to know all about him. But I do wish you'd let me rest a bit first. Your language is still not familiar to me. I had to learn them all, quite exhausting.

POWERS: You speak *all* our languages?

KRETON: Yes, all of them. But then it's easier than you might think since I can see what's inside.

POWERS: Speaking of what's inside, we're going to take your ship apart.

KRETON: Oh, I wish you wouldn't.

POWERS: Security demands it.

KRETON: In that case *my* security demands you leave it alone.

POWERS: You plan to stop us?

KRETON: I already have . . . Listen.

(far-off shouting. AIDE *rushes into the study.)*

AIDE: Something's happened to the ship, General. The door's shut and there's some kind of wall all around it, an invisible wall. We can't get near it.

KRETON: *(to camera)* I hope there was no one inside.

POWERS: *(to* KRETON*)* How did you do that?

KRETON: I couldn't begin to explain. Now if you don't mind, I think we should go in and see our hosts.

(He rises, goes into living room. POWERS *and* AIDE *look at each other.)*

POWERS: Don't let him out of your sight.

(Cut to living room as POWERS *picks up phone.* KRETON *is with* JOHN *and* ELLEN.*)*

KRETON: I don't mind curiosity but I really can't permit them to wreck my poor ship.

ELLEN: What do you plan to do, now you're here?

KRETON: Oh, keep busy. I have a project or two. . . . *(sighs)* I can't believe you're real!

JOHN: Then we're all in the same boat.

KRETON: Boat? Oh, yes! Well, I should have come ages ago but I . . . I couldn't get away until yesterday.

JOHN: Yesterday? It only took you a *day* to get here?

KRETON: One of *my* days, not yours. But then you don't know about time yet.

JOHN: Oh, you mean relativity.

KRETON: No, it's much more involved than that. You won't know about time until . . . now let me see if I remember . . . no, I don't, but it's about two thousand years.

JOHN: What do we do between now and then?

KRETON: You simply go on the way you are, living your exciting primitive lives . . . you have no idea how much fun you're having now.

ELLEN: I hope you'll stay with us while you're here.

KRETON: That's very nice of you. Perhaps I will. Though I'm sure you'll get tired of having a visitor underfoot all the time.

ELLEN: Certainly not. And Daddy will be deliriously happy. He can interview you by the hour.

JOHN: What's it like in outer space?

KRETON: Dull.

ELLEN: I should think it would be divine!

(POWERS *enters.*)

KRETON: No, General, it won't work.

POWERS: What won't work?

KRETON: Trying to blow up my little force field. You'll just plough up Mrs. Spelding's garden.

(POWERS *snarls.*)

ELLEN: Can you tell what we're *all* thinking?

KRETON: Yes. As a matter of fact, it makes me a bit giddy. Your minds are not at all like ours. You see we control our thoughts while you . . . well, it's extraordinary the things you think about!

ELLEN: Oh, how awful! You can tell *everything* we think?

KRETON: Everything! It's one of the reasons I'm here, to intoxicate myself with your primitive minds . . . with the wonderful rawness of your emotions! You have no idea how it excites me! You simply seethe with unlikely emotions.

ELLEN: I've never felt so sordid.

JOHN: From now on I'm going to think about agriculture.

SPELDING: *(entering)* You would.

ELLEN: Daddy!

KRETON: No, no. You must go right on thinking about Ellen. Such wonderfully *purple* thoughts!

SPELDING: Now see here, Powers, you're carrying this martial law thing too far. . . .

POWERS: Unfortunately, until I have received word from Washington as to the final disposition of this problem, you must obey my orders: no telephone calls, no communication with the outside.

SPELDING: This is unsupportable.

KRETON: Poor Mr. Spelding! If you like, I shall go. That would solve everything, wouldn't it?

POWERS: You're not going anywhere, Mr. Kreton, until I've had my instruction.

KRETON: I sincerely doubt if you could stop me. However, I put it up to Mr. Spelding. Shall I go?

SPELDING: Yes! (POWERS *gestures a warning.*) Do stay, I mean, we want you to get a good impression of us. . . .

KRETON: And of course you still want to be the first journalist to interview me. Fair enough. All right, I'll stay on for a while.

POWERS: Thank you.

KRETON: Don't mention it.

SPELDING: General, may I ask our guest a few questions?

POWERS: Go right ahead, Roger. I hope you'll do better than I did.

SPELDING: Since you read our minds, you probably already know what our fears are.

KRETON: I do, yes.

SPELDING: We are afraid that you represent a hostile race.

KRETON: And I have assured General Powers that my people are not remotely hostile. Except for me, no one is interested in this planet's present stage.

SPELDING: Does this mean you might be interested in a *later* stage?

KRETON: I'm not permitted to discuss your future. Of course my friends think me perverse to be interested in a primitive society but there's no accounting for tastes, is there? You are my hobby. I love you. And that's all there is to it.

POWERS: So you're just here to look around . . . sort of going native.

KRETON: What a nice expression! That's it exactly. I am going native.

POWERS: *(grimly)* Well, it is my view that you have been sent here by another civilization for the express purpose of reconnoitering prior to invasion.

KRETON: That *would* be your view! The wonderfully

primitive assumption that all strangers are hostile. You're almost too good to be true, General.

POWERS: You deny your people intend to make trouble for us?

KRETON: I deny it.

POWERS: Then are they interested in establishing communication with us? Trade? That kind of thing?

KRETON: We have always had communication with you. As for trade, well, we do not trade . . . that is something peculiar only to your social level. *(quickly)* Which I'm not criticizing! As you know, I approve of everything you do.

POWERS: I give up.

SPELDING: You have no interest then in . . . well, trying to dominate the earth.

KRETON: Oh, yes!

POWERS: I thought you just said your people weren't interested in us.

KRETON: *They're* not, but *I* am.

POWERS: You!

KRETON: Me . . . I mean I. You see I've come here to take charge.

POWERS: Of the United States?

KRETON: No, of the whole world. I'm sure you'll be much happier and it will be great fun for me. You'll get used to it in no time.

POWERS: This is ridiculous. How can one man take over the world?

KRETON: *(gaily)* Wait and see!

POWERS: *(to* AIDE*)* Grab him!

*(*POWERS *and* AIDE *rush* KRETON *but within a foot of him, they stop, stunned.)*

KRETON: You can't touch me. That's part of the game. *(He yawns.)* Now, if you don't mind, I shall go up to my room for a little lie-down.

SPELDING: I'll show you the way.

KRETON: That's all right, I know the way. *(touches his brow.)* Such savage thoughts! My head is vibrating like a drum. I feel quite giddy, all of you thinking away. *(He starts to the door; he pauses beside* MRS. SPELDING.*)* No, its not a dream dear lady. I shall be

here in the morning when you wake up. And now, good night, dear, wicked children. . . .
(He goes as we fade out.)

ACT TWO

(Fade in on KRETON*'s bedroom next morning. He lies fully clothed on bed with cat on his lap.)*

KRETON: Poor cat! Of course I sympathize with you. Dogs *are* distasteful. What? Oh, I can well believe they do: yes, yes, how disgusting. They don't ever groom their fur! But you do *constantly,* such a fine coat. No, no, I'm not just saying that. I really mean it: exquisite texture. Of course, I wouldn't say it was *nicer* than skin but even so. . . . What? Oh, no! They *chase* you! Dogs chase you for no reason at all except pure malice? You poor creature. Ah, but you *do* fight back! That's right! Give it to them: slash, bite, scratch! Don't let them get away with a trick. . . . No! Do dogs really do that? Well, I'm sure *you* don't. What . . . oh, well, yes I completely agree about mice. They *are* delicious! (Ugh!) Pounce, snap and there is a heavenly dinner. No, I don't know any mice yet . . . they're not very amusing? But after all think how you must terrify them because you are so bold, so cunning, so beautifully predatory!
(knock at door)
Come in.

ELLEN: *(enters)* Good morning. I brought you your breakfast.

KRETON: How thoughtful! *(examines bacon)* Delicious, but I'm afraid my stomach is not like yours, if you'll pardon me. I don't eat. *(removes pill from his pocket and swallows it)* This is all I need for the day. *(indicates cat)* Unlike this creature, who would eat her own weight every hour, given a chance.

ELLEN: How do you know?

KRETON: We've had a talk.

ELLEN: You can *speak* to the cat?

KRETON: Not speak exactly but we communicate. I look

inside and the cat cooperates. Bright red thoughts, very exciting, though rather on one level.

ELLEN: Does kitty like us?

KRETON: No, I wouldn't say she did. But then she has very few thoughts not concerned with food. Have you, my quadruped criminal? *(He strokes the cat, which jumps to the floor.)*

ELLEN: You know you've really upset everyone.

KRETON: I supposed that I would.

ELLEN: Can you really take over the world, just like that?

KRETON: Oh, yes.

ELLEN: What do you plan to do when you *have* taken over?

KRETON: Ah, that is my secret.

ELLEN: Well, I think you'll be a very nice President, *if* they let you of course.

KRETON: What a sweet girl you are! Marry him right away.

ELLEN: Marry John?

KRETON: Yes. I see it in your head *and* in his. He wants you very much.

ELLEN: Well, we plan to get married this summer, if father doesn't fuss too much.

KRETON: Do it before then. I shall arrange it all if you like.

ELLEN: How?

KRETON: I can convince your father.

ELLEN: That sounds awfully ominous. I think you'd better leave poor Daddy alone.

KRETON: Whatever you say. *(sighs)* Oh, I love it so! When I woke up this morning I had to pinch myself to prove I was really here.

ELLEN: We were all doing a bit of pinching too. Ever since dawn we've had nothing but visitors and phone calls and troops outside in the garden. No one has the faintest idea what to do about you.

KRETON: Well, I don't think they'll be confused much longer.

ELLEN: How do you plan to conquer the world?

KRETON: I confess I'm not sure. I suppose I must make some demonstration of strength, some colorful trick that will frighten everyone . . . though I much prefer taking charge quietly. That's why I've sent for the President.

ELLEN: The President? *Our* President?

KRETON: Yes, he'll be along any minute now.

ELLEN: But the President just doesn't go around visiting people.

KRETON: He'll visit me. *(chuckles)* It may come as a surprise to him, but he'll be in this house in a very few minutes. I think we'd better go downstairs now. *[To cat.]* No, I will not give you a mouse. You must get your own. Be self-reliant. Beast!

(Dissolve to the study. POWERS *is reading book entitled:* The Atom and You. *Muffled explosions off stage.)*

AIDE: *(entering)* Sir, nothing seems to be working. Do we have the General's permission to try a fission bomb on the force field?

POWERS: No . . . no. We'd better give it up.

AIDE: The men are beginning to talk.

POWERS: *(thundering)* Well, keep them quiet! *(contritely)* I'm sorry, Captain. I'm on edge. Fortunately, the whole business will soon be in the hands of the World Council.

AIDE: What will the World Council do?

POWERS: It will be interesting to observe them.

AIDE: You don't think this Kreton can really take over the world, do you?

POWERS: Of course not. Nobody can.

(Dissolve to living room, MRS. SPELDING *and* SPELDING *are talking.)*

MRS. SPELDING: You still haven't asked Mr. Kreton about moving that thing, have you?

SPELDING: There are too many *important* things to ask him.

MRS. SPELDING: I hate to be a nag but you know the trouble I have had getting anything to grow in that part of the garden . . .

JOHN: *(enters)* Good morning.

MRS. SPELDING: Good morning, John.

JOHN: Any sign of your guest?

MRS. SPELDING: Ellen took his breakfast up to him a few minutes ago.

JOHN: They don't seem to be having much luck, do they? I sure hope you don't mind my staying here like this.

(SPELDING *glowers.*)

MRS. SPELDING: Why, we love having you! I just hope your family aren't too anxious.

JOHN: One of the G.I.'s finally called them, said I was staying here for the weekend.

SPELDING: The rest of our *lives,* if something isn't done soon.

JOHN: Just how long do you think that'll be, Dad?

SPELDING: Who knows?

(KRETON *and* ELLEN *enter.*)

KRETON: Ah, how wonderful to see you again! Let me catch my breath. . . . Oh, your minds! It's not easy for me, you know. So many crude thoughts blazing away! Yes, Mrs. Spelding, I will move the ship off your roses.

MRS. SPELDING: That's awfully sweet of you.

KRETON: Mr. Spelding, if any interviews are to be granted you will be the first. I promise you.

SPELDING: That's very considerate, I'm sure.

KRETON: So you can stop thinking *those* particular thoughts. And now where is the President?

SPELDING: The President?

KRETON: Yes, I sent for him. He should be here. *(He goes to the terrace window.)* Ah, that must be he.

(A swarthy man in uniform with a sash across his chest is standing, bewildered, on the terrace. KRETON *opens the glass doors.)*

Come in, sir, come in, Your Excellency. Good of you to come on such short notice.

(MAN *enters.*)

MAN: *(in Spanish accent)* Where am I?

KRETON: You *are* the President, aren't you?

MAN: Of course I am the President. What am I doing here? I was dedicating a bridge and I find myself. . . .

KRETON: *(aware of his mistake)* Oh, dear! *Where* was the bridge?

MAN: Where do you think, you idiot, in Paraguay!

KRETON: *(to others)* I seem to've made a mistake. Wrong President. *(Gestures, and the* MAN *disappears)* Seemed rather upset, didn't he?

JOHN: You can make people come and go just like that?

KRETON: Just like that.

(POWERS *looks into room from the study.)*

POWERS: Good morning, Mr. Kreton. Could I see you for a moment?

KRETON: By all means. *(He crosses to the study.)*

SPELDING: I believe I am going mad.

(Cut to study. The AIDE *stands at attention while* POWERS *addresses* KRETON.*)*

POWERS: . . . and so we feel, the government of the United States feels, that this problem is too big for any one country, therefore we are turning the whole affair over to Paul Laurent, the Secretary-General of the World Council.

KRETON: Very sensible. I should've thought of that myself.

POWERS: Mr. Laurent is on his way here now. And I may add, Mr. Kreton, you've made me look singularly ridiculous.

KRETON: I'm awfully sorry. *(pause)* No, you can't kill me.

POWERS: You were reading my mind again.

KRETON: I can't really help it, you know. And such *black* thoughts today, but intense, very intense.

POWERS: I regard you as a menace.

KRETON: I know you do and I think it's awfully unkind. I do mean well.

POWERS: Then go back where you came from and leave us alone.

KRETON: I'm afraid I can't do that just yet. . . .

(Phone rings, the AIDE *answers it.)*

AIDE: He's outside? Sure, let him through. *(to* POWERS*)* The Secretary-General of the World Council is here sir.

POWERS: *(to* KRETON*)* I hope you'll listen to *him.*

KRETON: Oh, I shall, of course. I love listening.

(*The door opens and* PAUL LAURENT, *middle-aged and serene, enters.* POWERS *and his* AIDE *stand to attention.* KRETON *goes forward to shake hands.*)

LAURENT: Mr. Kreton?

KRETON: At your service, Mr. Laurent.

LAURENT: I welcome you to this planet in the name of the World Council.

KRETON: Thank you sir, thank you.

LAURENT: Could you leave us alone for a moment, General?

POWERS: Yes, sir.

(POWERS *and* AIDE *go.* LAURENT *smiles at* KRETON.)

LAURENT: Shall we sit down?

KRETON: Yes, yes I love sitting down. I'm afraid my manners are not quite suitable, yet.

(*They sit down.*)

LAURENT: Now, Mr. Kreton, in violation of all the rules of diplomacy, may I come to the point?

KRETON: You may.

LAURENT: Why are you here?

KRETON: Curiosity. Pleasure.

LAURENT: You are a tourist then in this time and place?

KRETON: (*nods*) Yes. Very well put.

LAURENT: We have been informed that you have extraordinary powers.

KRETON: By your standards, yes, they must seem extraordinary.

LAURENT: We have also been informed that it is your intention to . . . to take charge of this world.

KRETON: That is correct. . . . What a remarkable mind you have! I have difficulty looking inside it.

LAURENT: (*laughs*) Practice. I've attended so many conferences. . . . May I say that your conquest of our world puts your status of tourist in a rather curious light?

KRETON: Oh, I said nothing about *conquest*.

LAURENT: Then how else do you intend to govern? The people won't allow you to direct their lives without a struggle.

KRETON: But I'm sure they will if I ask them to.

LAURENT: You believe you can do all this without, well, without violence?

KRETON: Of course I can. One or two demonstrations and I'm sure they'll do as I ask. *(smiles)* Watch this.

(Pause: Then shouting. POWERS *bursts into room.)*

POWERS: Now what've you done?

KRETON: Look out the window, your Excellency.

*(*LAURENT *goes to window. A rifle floats by, followed by an alarmed soldier.)*

Nice, isn't it? I confess I worked out a number of rather melodramatic tricks last night. Incidentally, all the rifles of all the soldiers in all the world are now floating in the air. *(gestures)* Now they have them back.

POWERS: *(to* LAURENT*)* You see, sir, I didn't exaggerate in my report.

LAURENT: *(awed)* No, no, you certainly didn't.

KRETON: You were sceptical, weren't you?

LAURENT: Naturally. But now I . . . now I think it's possible.

POWERS: That this . . . this gentleman is going to run everything?

LAURENT: Yes, yes I do. And it might be wonderful.

KRETON: You *are* more clever than the others. You begin to see that I mean only good.

LAURENT: Yes, only good. General, do you realize what this means? We can have one government. . . .

KRETON: With innumerable bureaus, and intrigue. . . .

LAURENT: *(excited)* And the whole world could be incredibly prosperous, especially if he'd help us with his superior knowledge.

KRETON: *(delighted)* I will, I will. I'll teach you to look into one another's minds. You'll find it devastating but enlightening: all that self-interest, those *lurid* emotions. . . .

LAURENT: No more countries. No more wars. . . .

KRETON: *(startled)* What? Oh, but I like a lot of countries. Besides, at this stage of your development you're supposed to have lots of countries and lots of wars . . . innumerable wars. . . .

LAURENT: But you can help us change all that.

KRETON: *Change* all that! My dear sir, I am your friend.

LAURENT: What do you mean?

KRETON: Why, your deepest pleasure is violence. How

can you deny that? It is the whole point to you, the whole point to my hobby . . . and you are my hobby, all mine.

LAURENT: But our lives are devoted to *controlling* violence, and not creating it.

KRETON: Now, don't take me for an utter fool. After all, I can see into your minds. My dear fellow, don't you *know* what you are?

LAURENT: What are we?

KRETON: You are savages. I have returned to the dark ages of an insignificant planet simply because I want the glorious excitement of being among you and reveling in your savagery! There is murder in all your hearts and I love it! It intoxicates me!

LAURENT: *(slowly)* You hardly flatter us.

KRETON: I didn't mean to be rude but you did ask me why I am here and I've told you.

LAURENT: You have no wish then to . . . to help us poor savages.

KRETON: I couldn't even if I wanted to. You won't be civilized for at least two thousand years and you won't reach the level of my people for about a million years.

LAURENT: *(sadly)* Then you have come here only to . . . to observe?

KRETON: No, more than that. I mean to regulate your pastimes. But don't worry: I won't upset things too much. I've decided I don't want to be known to the people. You will go right on with your countries, your squabbles, the way you always have, while I will *secretly* regulate things through you.

LAURENT: The World Council does not govern. We only advise.

KRETON: Well, I shall advise you and you will advise the governments and we shall have a lovely time.

LAURENT: I don't know what to say. You obviously have the power to do as you please.

KRETON: I'm glad you realize that. Poor General Powers is now wondering if a hydrogen bomb might destroy me. It won't, General.

POWERS: Too bad.

KRETON: Now, your Excellency, I shall stay in this house until you have laid the groundwork for my first project.

LAURENT: And what is that to be?

KRETON: A war! I want one of your really splendid wars, with all the trimmings, all the noise and the fire. . . .

LAURENT: A war! You're joking. Why at this moment we are working as hard as we know how *not* to have a war.

KRETON: But secretly you want one. After all, it's the one thing your little race does well. You'd hardly want me to deprive you of your simple pleasures, now would you?

LAURENT: I think you must be mad.

KRETON: Not mad, simply a philanthropist. Of course I myself shall get a great deal of pleasure out of a war (the vibrations must be incredible!) but I'm doing it mostly for you. So, if you don't mind, I want to arrange a few incidents, so we can get one started spontaneously.

LAURENT: I refuse.

KRETON: In that event, I shall select someone else to head the World Council. Someone who *will* start a war. I suppose there exist a few people here who might like the idea.

LAURENT: How can you do such a horrible thing to us? Can't you see that we don't want to be savages?

KRETON: But you have no choice. Anyway, you're just pulling my leg! I'm sure you want a war as much as the rest of them do and that's what you're going to get: the biggest war you've ever had!

LAURENT: *(stunned)* Heaven help us!

KRETON: *(exuberant)* Heaven won't! Oh, what fun it will be! I can hardly wait! *(He strikes the globe of the world a happy blow as we fade out.)*

ACT THREE

Fade in on the study, two weeks later. KRETON *is sitting at desk on which a map is spread out. He has a pair of dividers, some models of jet aircraft. Occasionally he pretends to dive-bomb, imitating the sound of a bomb going off.* POWERS *enters.*

POWERS: You wanted me, sir?

KRETON: Yes, I wanted those figures on radioactive fall-out.

POWERS: They're being made up now, sir. Anything else?

KRETON: Oh, my dear fellow, why do you dislike me so?

POWERS: I am your military aide, sir: I don't have to answer that question. It is outside the sphere of my duties.

KRETON: Aren't you at least happy about your promotion?

POWERS: Under the circumstances, no, sir.

KRETON: I find your attitude baffling.

POWERS: Is that all sir?

KRETON: You have never once said what you thought of my war plans. Not once have I got a single word of encouragement from you, a single compliment . . . only black thoughts.

POWERS: Since you read my mind, sir, you know what I think.

KRETON: True, but I can't help but feel that deep down inside of you there is just a twinge of professional jealousy. You don't like the idea of an outsider playing your game better than you do. Now confess!

POWERS: I am acting as your aide only under duress.

KRETON: *(sadly)* Bitter, bitter . . . and to think I chose you especially as my aide. Think of all the other generals who would give anything to have your job.

POWERS: Fortunately, they know nothing about my job.

KRETON: Yes, I do think it wise not to advertise my presence, don't you?

POWERS: I can't see that it makes much difference, since you seem bent on destroying our world.

KRETON: I'm not going to destroy it. A few dozen cities, that's all, and not very nice cities either. Think of the fun you'll have building new ones when it's over.

POWERS: How many millions of people do you plan to kill?

KRETON: Well, quite a few, but they love this sort of thing. You can't convince me they don't. Oh, I know what Laurent says. But he's a misfit, out of step with this time. Fortunately, my new World Council is more reasonable.

POWERS: Paralyzed is the word, sir.

KRETON: You don't think they like me either?

POWERS: You *know* they hate you, sir.

KRETON: But love and hate are so confused in your savage minds and the vibrations of the one are so very like those of the other that I can't always distinguish. You see, we neither love nor hate in my world. We simply have hobbies. *(He strokes the globe of the world tenderly.)* But now to work. Tonight's the big night: first, the sneak attack, then: boom! *(He claps his hands gleefully.)*

(Dissolve to the living room, to John and Ellen.)

ELLEN: I've never felt so helpless in my life.

JOHN: Here we all stand around doing nothing while he plans to blow up the world.

ELLEN: Suppose we went to the newspapers.

JOHN: He controls the press. When Laurent resigned they didn't even print his speech. *(gloomy pause)*

ELLEN: What are you thinking about, John?

JOHN: Walnuts. *(They embrace.)*

ELLEN: Can't we do anything?

JOHN: No, I guess there's nothing.

ELLEN: *(vehemently)* Oh! I could kill him!

(Kreton and Powers enter.)

KRETON: Very good, Ellen, *very* good! I've never felt you so violent.

ELLEN: You heard what I said to John?

KRETON: Not in words, but you were absolutely bathed in malevolence.

POWERS: I'll get the papers you wanted, sir.

(Powers exits.)

KRETON: I don't think he likes me very much but your father does. Only this morning he offered to handle my public relations and I said I'd let him. Wasn't that nice of him?

JOHN: I think I'll go get some fresh air. *(He goes out through the terrace door)*

KRETON: Oh, dear! *(sighs)* Only your father is really

entering the spirit of the game. He's a much better sport than you, my dear.

ELLEN: *(exploding)* Sport! That's it! You think we're sport. You think we're animals to be played with: well, we're not. We're people and we don't want to be destroyed.

KRETON: *(patiently)* But *I* am not destroying you. You will be destroying one another of your own free will, as you have always done. I am simply a . . . a kibitzer.

ELLEN: No, you are a vampire!

KRETON: A vampire? You mean I drink blood? Ugh!

ELLEN: No, you drink emotions, our emotions. You'll sacrifice us all for the sake of your . . . your vibrations!

KRETON: Touché. Yet what harm am I really doing? It's true I'll enjoy the war more than anybody; but it will be *your* destructiveness after all, not mine.

ELLEN: You could stop it.

KRETON: So could you.

ELLEN: I?

KRETON: Your race. They could stop altogether but they won't. And I can hardly intervene in their natural development. The most I can do is help out in small, practical ways.

ELLEN: We are not what you think. We're not so . . . so primitive.

KRETON: My dear girl, just take this one household: your mother dislikes your father but she is too tired to do anything about it so she knits and she gardens and she tries not to think about him. Your father, on the other hand, is bored with all of you. Don't look shocked: he doesn't like you any more than you like him. . . .

ELLEN: Don't say that!

KRETON: I am only telling you the truth. Your father wants you to marry someone important; therefore he objects to John while you, my girl. . . .

ELLEN: *(With a fierce cry,* ELLEN *grabs vase to throw.)* You devil! *(Vase breaks in her hand.)*

KRETON: You see? That proves my point perfectly. *(gently)* Poor savage, I cannot help what you are.

(briskly) Anyway, you will soon be distracted from personal problems. Tonight is the night. If you're a good girl, I'll let you watch the bombing.

(Dissolve to study: Eleven forty-five. POWERS *and the* AIDE *gloomily await the war.)*

AIDE: General, isn't there anything we can do?

POWERS: It's out of our hands.

(KRETON, *dressed as a Hussar with shako, enters.)*

KRETON: Everything on schedule?

POWERS: Yes, sir. Planes left for their targets at twenty-two hundred.

KRETON: Good . . . good. I myself, shall take off shortly after midnight to observe the attack first hand.

POWERS: Yes, sir.

(KRETON *goes into the living-room where the family is gloomily assembled.)*

KRETON:*(enters from study)* And now the magic hour approaches! I hope you're all as thrilled as I am.

SPELDING: You still won't tell us who's attacking whom?

KRETON: You'll know in exactly . . . fourteen minutes.

ELLEN: *(bitterly)* Are we going to be killed too?

KRETON: Certainly not! You're quite safe, at least in the early stages of the war.

ELLEN: Thank you.

MRS. SPELDING: I suppose this will mean rationing again.

SPELDING: Will . . . will we see anything from here?

KRETON: No, but there should be a good picture on the monitor in the study. Powers is tuning in right now.

JOHN: *(at window)* Hey look, up there! Coming this way! *(Ellen joins him.)*

ELLEN: What is it?

JOHN: Why . . . it's *another* one! And it's going to land.

KRETON:*(surprised)* I'm sure your mistaken. No one would dream of coming here. *(He has gone to the window, too.)*

ELLEN: It's landing!

SPELDING: Is it a friend of yours, Mr. Kreton?

KRETON: *(slowly)* No, no, not a friend. . . . (KRETON *retreats to the study; he inadvertently drops a lace handerchief beside the sofa.)*

JOHN: Here he comes.
ELLEN: *(suddenly bitter)* Now we have two of them.
MRS. SPELDING: My poor roses.

(The new VISITOR *enters in a gleam of light from his ship. He is wearing a most futuristic costume. Without a word, he walks past the awed family into the study.* KRETON *is cowering behind the globe.* POWERS *and the* AIDE *stare, bewildered, as the* VISITOR *gestures sternly and* KRETON *reluctantly removes shako and sword. They communicate by odd sounds.)*

VISITOR: *(to* POWERS*)* Please leave us alone.

(Cut to living room as POWERS *and the* AIDE *enter from the study.)*

POWERS: *(to* ELLEN*)* Who on earth was that?
ELLEN: It's another one, another visitor.
POWERS: Now we're done for.
ELLEN: I'm going in there.
MRS. SPELDING: Ellen, don't you dare!
ELLEN: I'm going to talk to them. *(starts to door)*
JOHN: I'm coming, too.
ELLEN: *(grimly)* No, alone. I know what I want to say.

(Cut to interior of the study, to KRETON *and the other* VISITOR *as* ELLEN *enters.)*

ELLEN: I want you both to listen to me. . . .
VISITOR: You don't need to speak. I know what you will say.
ELLEN: That you have no right here? That you mustn't. . . .
VISITOR: I agree. Kreton has no right here. He is well aware that it is forbidden to interfere with the past.
ELLEN: The past?
VISITOR: *(nods)* You are the past, the dark ages: we are from the future. In fact, we are *your* descendants on another planet. We visit you from time to time but we never interfere because it would change *us* if we did. Fortunately, I have arrived in time.
ELLEN: There won't be a war?
VISITOR: There will be no war. And there will be no memory of any of this. When we leave here you will forget Kreton and me. Time will turn back to the moment before his arrival.

ELLEN: Why did you want to hurt us?

KRETON: (*heartbroken*) Oh, but I didn't! I only wanted to have . . . well, to have a little fun, to indulge my hobby . . . against the rules of course.

VISITOR: (*to Ellen*) Kreton is a rarity among us. Mentally and morally he is retarded. He is a child and he regards your period as his toy.

KRETON: A child, now really!

VISITOR: He escaped from his nursery and came back in time to you. . . .

KRETON: And *every*thing went wrong, everything! I wanted to visit 1860 . . . that's my *real* period but then something happened to the car and I ended up here, not that I don't find you nearly as interesting but. . . .

VISITOR: We must go, Kreton.

KRETON: *(to* ELLEN*)* You did like me just a bit, didn't you?

ELLEN: Yes, yes I did, until you let your hobby get out of hand. *(to* VISITOR*)* What is the future like?

VISITOR: Very serene, very different. . . .

KRETON: Don't believe him: it is dull, dull, dull beyond belief! One simply floats through eternity: no wars, no excitement. . . .

VISITOR: It is forbidden to discuss these matters.

KRETON: I can't see what difference it makes since she's going to forget all about us anyway.

ELLEN: Oh, how I'd love to see the future. . . .

VISITOR: It is against. . . .

KRETON: Against the rules: how tiresome, you are. *(to* ELLEN*)* But, alas, you can never pay us a call because you aren't born yet! I mean where we are you are not. Oh, Ellen, dear, think kindly of me, until you forget.

ELLEN: I will.

VISITOR: Come. Time has begun to turn back. Time is bending.

(He starts to door. KRETON *turns conspiratorially to* ELLEN.*)*

KRETON: Don't be sad, my girl. I shall be back one bright day, but a bright day in 1860. I dote on the Civil War, so exciting. . . .

VISITOR: Kreton!

KRETON: Only next time I think it'll be more fun if the *South* wins! *(He hurries after the* VISITOR.*)*

(Cut to clock as the hands spin backwards. Dissolve to the living room, exactly the same as the first scene: SPELDING, MRS. SPELDING, ELLEN.*)*

SPELDING: There is nothing wrong with marrying a wealthy man. The horror of it has always eluded me. However, my only wish is that you marry someone hard-working, ambitious, a man who'll make his mark in the world. Not a boy who is content to sit on a farm all his life, growing peanuts. . . .

ELLEN: English walnuts! And he won't just sit there.

SPELDING: Will you stop contradicting me?

ELLEN: But, Daddy, John grows walnuts. . . .

*(*JOHN *enters.)*

JOHN: Hello, everybody.

MRS. SPELDING: Good evening, John.

ELLEN: What kept you, darling? You missed Daddy's broadcast.

JOHN: I saw it before I left home. Wonderful broadcast, sir.

SPELDING: Thank you, John.

*(*JOHN *crosses to window.)*

JOHN: That meteor you were talking about, well, for a while it looked almost like a space ship or something. You can just barely see it now.

(Ellen joins him at window. They watch, arms about one another.)

SPELDING: Space ship! Nonsense! Remarkable what some people will believe, *want* to believe. Besides, as I said in the broadcast: if there's any traveling to be done in space we'll do it first.

(He notices KRETON'S *handerchief on sofa and picks it up. They all look at it, puzzled, as we cut to stock shot of the starry night against which two space ships vanish in the distance, one serene in its course, the other erratic, as we fade out.)*

PRODUCTION

TELEVISION TECHNIQUES

The mobility of the camera, although it offers the director certain opportunities, presents him with special problems.

1/ What instructions has Vidal included in his script for the *cameramen?* (Look up technical terms with which you are unfamiliar.) Do you think it is more difficult to write a radio or a television script? Why?

2/ How would *the set* for a television play differ from that for a stage play? Keep the camera's movements in mind.

3/ Why is *lighting* as important in filming a television play as in producing a stage play?

4/ Watch an episode of a popular television show.

How frequently did the director have the camera move about the set?

Why was each of these moves made?

5/ What television shows depend for their appeal on *special technical effects*? How do you think these effects are achieved?

6/ *How many actors* were there in the television program you watched?

Why do you think there were not more characters introduced?

7/ How has Vidal tried to ensure that the television viewer will *continue* watching his play, despite the inevitable interruptions for commercials?

REVIEW

Compose a short review of "Visit to a Small Planet" as if you were a newspaper television critic who had viewed the first telecast of the play on the night of May 8, 1955.

RESEARCH

1/ How do you account for the continuing popularity of *science fiction* television shows, movies and novels?

2/ Read one of the following plays which also deals with a disconcerting visitor: Noel Coward's *Blithe Spirit* or *The Man Who Came to Dinner.*

What similarities do you find between the play you read and Vidal's "Visit to a Small Planet"?

READING

1/ Two different kinds of visitors from outer space figure prominently in *Blithe Spirit* (in *Three Plays by Noel Coward,* Dell Delta paperback 6437) and *The Man Who Came to Dinner,* by George S. Kaufman and Moss Hart (available in script form from Dramatists' Play Service, 14 E. 38th Street, New York, N. Y.).

2/ Gore Vidal has collected eight complete one-hour dramas by outstanding television writers in *Best Television Plays* (A Ballantine Bal-Hi paperback U2804).

EPILOGUE: THE WEANS ROBERT NATHAN

A CBS RADIO WORKSHOP PLAY

The Weans

Characters

Radio Rhodesia reporters	*archaeologists*
ANNOUNCER	B'HAN BOLLEK
DINAR GEB	HANH SHUI
HULAY BENEKER	BES NEF
YUSH ERTEBBE	HAPH-BUKONG
KOWLY DEE	NAT OBELGERST-LEVY
	ASSISTANT

ANNOUNCER: This is Radio Rhodesia, broadcasting on the mega, mico and strato beams. We take you now to the Ethnical Museum of Antiquity at Kenya, and our correspondent Dinar Geb. Come in, Dinar Geb. . . . *(pause)* Stand by, please, we are trying to get through. Radio Rhodesia to Dinar Geb . . . come in, Dinar Geb. . . .

GEB: This is Dinar Geb, speaking from the Great Hall of the Ethnical Museum of Antiquity at Kenya. If my voice sounds a little strange to you, it's because I have become infected with the excitement of the scholars gathered here to receive the reports from the field expeditions on the Great West Continent. As you know, as part of the world-wide celebration of this Astro-Physical year of 7956 A.D., teams of archeologists have been working for months in the *tumuli,* or city mounds, of this uninhabited continent. Our staff correspondents are with them now, at the tumulus of n.yok, at Cha'ago, at Loose Angles, and at Pound-Laundry. In just a moment you will hear them in person, but first. . . . Standing beside me at this microphone is S'ra B'Han Bollek, Chancellor of Education and Curator of the Museum. S'ra Bollek, would you care to give our listeners some hint as to what discoveries may be announced today?

BOLLEK: No, S'ra Geb, that would be cheating. But I will say this—I believe we have come a great distance in understanding the Weans since the first artifacts were dug up in the city mound of Boxtin nearly two hundred years ago.

GEB: They are the ones in this glass case, are they not?

BOLLEK: That's right—an ivory cross attached to some beads, and a rusted iron wheel, apparently designed to run along some kind of track. Scarcely enough upon which to postulate a culture, or project a civilization.

GEB: But since then, other discoveries have been made.

BOLLEK: Oh, yes. From time to time hunters, prospectors, and other adventurers have returned from that deserted and forbidding land with fragments of scrolls —but they were completely meaningless hieroglyphs until the discovery some years ago of the talking Disc of Oleens.

GEB: In one of your monographs, didn't you liken the Disc of Oleens to the Rosetta Stone?

BOLLEK: Indeed I did. Except that the Disc of Oleens speaks, whereas the Rosetta Stone could only be read.

GEB: I'm afraid I'm a little rusty on my ancient history, S'ra Bollek. I wonder if you'd mind telling our listeners just what the Rosetta Stone is—or was.

BOLLEK: Gladly. The Rosetta Stone was discovered in Egypt more than six thousand years ago in the year 1799 A.D. by the soldiers of the war lord Na Po Lee On. It was inscribed in Egyptian hieroglyphs, along with Greek and Roman glyphs. A brilliant sage of antiquity, Sham Py Own, discerned the similarity, and thus found the key to the Egyptian language. A shattering piece of scholarship, but no less brilliant than work of my esteemed colleague S'ra Hanh Shui in analyzing the message of the Disc of Oleens.

GEB: Oleens? That's the city mound at the extreme south of the Great West Continent, isn't it?

BOLLEK: Exactly at the mouth of the great dry river, the Misses. It was there in the winter of 7940 that an expedition under Hanh Shui discovered the disc, in an astonishing state of preservation. Since the Disc of Oleens gave us our first indication of the identity of the people of We, I thought perhaps it would not be inappropriate to play it now.

GEB: Excellent. Is that the original you have there?

BOLLEK: Oh, my, no! This is a copy—a transcription of it. The original is never removed from the vaults of the museum. But it is a faithful copy. Listen.

WEAN: *(filter—bad and scratchy)* "Now we'uns knows, and they'uns knows, too, down deep in they'uns' hearts—"

GEB: Well, that's mighty interesting. S'ra Bollek. Mighty interesting. But—what does it mean?

BOLLEK: Mean? Well its actual meaning is obscure. But the human voice speaking to us from six thousand years ago—utters on this disc the sound of every letter symbol in all the glyphs and scrolls we have discovered. We know now, Sra Geb, that these ancient people, who so often inscribed their scrolls with the letters U.S.A., called their land the Us—or the We, and that they referred to themselves as Weuns—or Weans. Yes, we can thank S'ra Hanh Shui for giving us the key which unlocked this mystery—and that reminds me of an incident that occurred when Hanh Shui and I were students at the graduate school at Khartoum—

GEB: Yes—well, perhaps we will have time to hear it later, but I believe S'ra Hanh Shui is at the city mound of Cha'ago right now with our Radio Rhodesia reporter Hulay Beneker. Take it away, Hulay.

HULAY: *(heavy filter which clears gradually)* Thank you, Dinar Geb. This is Hulay Beneker at the Cha'ago excavation. I would like to describe the setting for you. A brazen sun bakes this desolate and salted land. This city mound Cha'ago lies at the western end of an ancient salt lake which appears to stretch endlessly toward the horizon—a forbidding sink of glittering white crystals, upon which not even the scrubby vegetation indigenous to this worthless continent dares to grow. . . . Well, so much for the description. I know all of you back home want to know the results of this expedition—and here is the man who can tell you, the distinguished professor and dean of the Advanced School of Primitive Languages of Kenya University, S'ra Hanh Shui.

SHUI: Greetings to my colleagues in the field, as well as back home. This is indeed a great and proud day for me. I have found another disc. Just as the talking Disc of Oleens gave us the secret of the Weans' language, I believe this Singing Disc of Cha'ago may indicate what the music of the Weans was.

HULAY: There seems to be an inscription on it, S'ra Shui.

SHUI: Yes. The nearest I can make out is *"Blew Sway Shoo by A—vis—Paisley. Sold a mill—yon cop—ees."*

HULAY: What does it mean?

SHUI: I haven't the slightest idea—but let's listen.

RECORD: *Elvis Presley recording. Screams of bobby-soxers.*

HULAY: That's music?

SHUI: Primitive, isn't it? Most rudimentary.

BOLLEK: *(filter)* Hello, friend Shui, can you hear me?

SHUI: Yes, who is it?

BOLLEK: B'Han Bollek at Kenya. Congratulations on your find.

SHUI: Thank you, my old friend.

BOLLEK: But I'm afraid you're mistaken.

SHUI: Mistaken?

BOLLEK: Yes. That's not music—that's a religious ceremony.

SHUI: What!

BOLLEK: Yes, you have misread the inscription. It is not *Avis Paisley*—it must be *Ephus Fressley.*

SHUI: *Fressley?*

BOLLEK: Yes, don't you remember my translation of the n.yok scroll regarding a great religious festival? I quote: "And Fressley threw his head back and commenced, and he did cause them to rock and roll, to give out cries and screams, loudly in the aisles and corridors, all in syncope." Unquote.

SHUI: Right as always, S'ra Bollek. I had thought it was music.

BOLLEK: I doubt if the Weans had any music. But your find is more important, for it proves they had a religion.

HULAY: And now, after that unscheduled but mighty interesting interchange between two long-time friends and associates, we continue our report on the Weans from the far edge of the continent. . . . Our next pick-up is from Loose Angles, or as some translators prefer, Loose Ankles, at the edge of the great Western Ocean. We take you there now. The next voice you hear will be our staff correspondent, Yush Ertebbe.

YUSH: *(filter)* Thank you, Hulay Beneker in Cha'ago. This is Yush Ertebbe speaking to you from the excavations near the bleak brown hills of Loose Angles. And here beside me is the head of this particular expedition, the only woman scientist participating, S'ress Bes Nef, the brilliant dean of Advanced Femininity at the University of Zagorra.

BES NEF: Hello, there. I was most interested in the comments S'ra B'Han Bollek just made upon the religious significance of the find at the Cha'ago dig. Because out here we, too, have come upon objects which have led us to believe that the Weans did have a primitive religion.

YUSH: You are referring to the golden idols, S'ress Bes Nef?

BES NEF: Precisely. Repeatedly, in the kitchen middens of smaller communities surrounding Loose Angles, we have dug up these small gilded statues cast away among the pottery sherds and other refuse. The presence of so many of the golden fetishes indicates beyond a shadow of doubt the existence of a considerable cult of Oscar, as our translation of certain scrolls proves the god's name to be. So for several months we have been searching the temple of this god—particularly in this area of Holy—Wood, which would by its very name indicate that it was once a place of veneration and worship. I believe I can safely report to you today that we have unearthed the temple of Oscar. It is not large, as temples go, but it is distinguished from all others in archeological history in one important respect. One expects to read the record of vanished races on the walls or frescoed ceilings of ancient temples. Here the record has been placed on the floor. The court is laid out in squares, and in each square are the imprint of feet and hands and words.

YUSH: What do they signify, S'ress Bes Nef?

BES NEF: My specialty is archeology not hieroglyphs—but my guess is that they were incantations to the god Oscar—the footprints perhaps those of his priests—or perhaps sacrificial victims.

YUSH: Can you translate any of the words?

BES NEF: Well, I can try. Here's one that says *Glore—ee—yah—Swan—song*. Utter gibberish. And there's one beside what looks like an imprint of a large human nose—*Jim—mee . . . Dur—ant—ee.*

YUSH: Wouldn't that appear to indicate that these were victims rather than priests?

BES NEF: Possibly. Some of them, at least, appear to have been put through a humiliating ordeal to prove their devotion to Oscar. It may take years before we find the answer to this fascinating riddle.

YUSH: Thank you, S'ress Bes Nef. And now, this is Yush Ertebbe returning you to Dinar Geb in Kenya.

GEB: Back once more at the Great Hall of the Kenya Museum. S'ra Bollek has been joined by his colleague S'ra Haph-Bukong, of the Libya Academy of Geophysical Sciences. Well, S'ras, what do you think of the field reports so far?

BOLLEK: Splendid. Splendid. They substantiate my theory that the Weans had at least a semblance of culture.

BUKONG: They still leave unanswered the question of origin.

BOLLEK: Oh, don't think there's any longer much doubt about that, Bukong. They came from Brython of course.

BUKONG: Theory—theory. No substantiation.

BOLLEK: What about their language similarity? For example, the Brython glyph *bathe* means "to immerse." The corresponding Wean glyph is *bath*. Same meaning exactly. And consider the Brythonic and the Wean glyph for "to hold together." It is identical—*brace*. Thus, the Brythons used braces to hold up their garments, while the Wean braces were generally applied to the teeth of the young.

BUKONG: Not exactly identical functions.

BOLLEK: But identical meaning.

BUKONG: What about the glyph for "that which rises"?

BOLLEK: Well, of course, there are always exceptions—

BUKONG: The Brythonic is *lift* and the Wean *elevator*. Where is the common root? Why, it's as inconsistent as—as—your translation of the name of the Wean capital. Pound-Laundry, indeed.

BOLLEK: How else would you translate it? The glyph for *washing* means laundry—and the Wean glyph—*ton* stands for a unit of weight, hence *pound*. Pound-Laundry. You couldn't say Washing-ton. It wouldn't make any sense. Though I must confess, we have never learned what was washed at Pound-Laundry.

GEB: Well, S'ras, this is most interesting, but I am informed that the expedition at the n.yok site is ready to make its report. . . . we take you now to the city mound of n.yok, and our Radio Rhodesia correspondent Kowly Dee.

cut

DEE: *(heavy filter which clears gradually)* Kowly Dee speaking from n.yok dig. There seems no doubt now that this tumulus or city mound marks the site of perhaps the most populous city of the Weans. In fact, we have reason to believe that this present expedition under the leadership of S'ra Obelgerst-Levy has found the answer to the fate of the Weans, as well as the reason why they apparently clustered together on this small island in such great numbers just before their extinction. I had hoped to be able to have Obelgerst-Levy here to make his report to you in person, but just before the program went on the air, he was called away to mound x-5, where a large part of our force of diggers have been concentrating for several days upon a new discovery which may well be a tomb. While working upon the lintel of a great temple a few days ago, one of our party fell through a hole into what appeared to be a cave. He was not too badly injured, and before being rescued by his fellows he noted that this apparent cave was in reality a tunnel, along which ran steel rails. Recalling the iron wheel discovered at the Boxtin tumulus more than a century ago, S'ra Obelgerst-Levy deduced that such a wheel might have been intended to be used on such rails as these. He immediately entered the tunnel, exploring it for some distance until he found it blocked by rubble, the result of some cataclysm of antiquity. At this point, however, he unearthed a glyph which read *Turty Fort Treet*—and close by a descending gallery above which was a glyph which he translated as *Maces* or perhaps *May—Cees*. Excavation was immediately begun on this descending gallery, and it is there that—What's that? Excuse me, S'ras and S'resses. *(pause)* Oh, this is wonderful! It couldn't have been timed better. I have just received a message that S'ra Obelgerst-Levy has reached the third level beneath Turty Fort Treet and is about to open the door to the tomb of May-Cees. We take you there to hear it for yourself—take it away, S'ra Obelgerst-Levy.

LEVY: Thank you, Kowly Dee. Good evening to the S'ras and S'resses back home in Kenya, Tanganyika, Libya, and elsewhere. Here in n.yok, it is still early afternoon, but where we are one cannot tell—so black is this tunnel—whether it be day or night. We have been digging downward along this gallery from the tunnel with rails for nearly a week, and at last we have arrived at a sealed door. Above it is a glyph which translates phonetically as *May-Cees Bar-gan Base-ment*. Appears to be meaningless—though the glyph *Base-ment* could be interpreted *tomb* or *sepulchre*. Well, we shall break through this door now, and attempt to describe to you what, if anything, we find beyond. You may begin, men.

SOUND: *Crowbars on door.*

LEVY: Easy there—easy—

SOUND: *Breaking glass.*

LEVY: You clumsy idiots.

SOUND: *Burglar alarm.*

LEVY: What's that?

ASSISTANT: I don't know, S'ra Obelgerst-Levy. As soon as the door glass was broken—a warning perhaps—

LEVY: Nonsense.

ASSISTANT: I remember reading about what happened to the men who violated the tombs of the Egyptian Pharaohs.

LEVY: Do you really think these Weans can reach out across six thousand years and harm us?

ASSISTANT: No, S'ra, not really—but still, one wonders.

LEVY: Proceed with the opening.

DEE: *(fading in, out of breath)* I hope I'm not too late.

LEVY: No, no, Kowly Dee—just in time.

DEE: What do you think you may find here?

LEVY: I have no idea. Throw a light down there! Come.

SOUND: *Feet echoing on stairs.*

LEVY: *(awed)* Yes. Yes, it is indeed a tomb.

DEE: A tomb?

LEVY: Yes. Look. On these racks here—garments. Strange ancient garments—coats of fur. Symbols—*"One-nine-eight—Ree-duced-from-two-two-five."*

DEE: Yes—and over there—tiny effigies—tiny-wagons—

LEVY: And here, bowls and cooking pots—in perfect condition—

ASSISTANT: There appear to be more chambers beyond.

LEVY: Is there any indication of sarcophagi or mummies?

ASSISTANT: None so far, S'ra.

DEE: Mummies?

LEVY: Yes. You will recall that it was the custom of many ancient people to bury their kings along with their retinue and their household goods to assure them comfort and companionship in the next world. The Egyptians were the most advanced in these matters—up until now.

DEE: I'm afraid I don't follow you completely, S'ra Levy—and I'm sure our listeners would like an explanation—

LEVY: Oh, dear me, we are on the air, aren't we? I'd quite forgotten—Excuse me, S'ras and S'resses—I've been carried away by the amazing significance of this find. We have obviously penetrated the tomb of a great king, Pharaoh, president, whichever translation you prefer—of the Weans—a ruler named May-Cee. We are surrounded by the elegant appurtenances and riches of an ancient ruler—racks of garments of fur and wool, perfectly preserved in this cool sepulchre for six thousand years, garments to warm the potentate on his journey to eternity. We find kettles and pots of brightest white and yellow metal to prepare his food—we find mannequins almost doll-like—and their tiny wagons—effigies of the retinue which accompanied him on his journey—

ASSISTANT: Excuse me, S'ra Obelgerst-Levy—

LEVY: You have found the mummy of May-Cee?

ASSISTANT: No—but in this next chamber—something most strange. Great eyes . . . Come—

LEVY: Great eyes?

DEE: This is indeed a strange and wonderful sight, S'ras and S'resses. We are moving now from the main chamber of the tomb to a side chamber. The lights of the diggers are sweeping back and forth, and at each turn picking up another curious artifact—a boat with a wonderously small motor attached to it—goggles and flat triangular shoes—bows and arrows—and here a curious two-wheeled vehicle. . . . Now we are in the side chamber, and our light beams are reflected by rows and rows of gigantic glass eyes, each in its own polished box. What are they?

LEVY: I don't know. Each of them has a dial with numbers.

ASSISTANT: Be careful, please, S'ra—

LEVY: Today, we look down on the ages. It is no time to be prudent. Now, let me see—the dial is numbered from one to thirteen—of mystic significance, no doubt. Ah, it turns.

DEE: But nothing happens.

LEVY: True, but we are not Weans. These strange Cyclopean boxes must have held great significance for them.

ASSISTANT: See, S'ra Levy. Here on the wall is a glyph—

LEVY: Ah! yes. "*CBS Tell——eee——viz——on.*" Meaningless.

ASSISTANT: But see—the pictograph. A Wean and his she-Wean sit before the box. And in the box is the face of another Wean.

LEVY: Yes. Indeed then, they were eyes of some sort—

DEE: But did the Weans watch the eye, or did the eye watch the Weans?

LEVY: Only exhaustive research can answer such questions.

DEE: But S'ra Obelgerst-Levy—can you hazard a guess why so many of these eyes have been put in the tomb of the potentate May-Cee?

LEVY: Yes, but only a guess. He must have been a man so vain that even after death he wished to watch through these eyes what his people were doing—or he wished through these eyes that his people could watch him. Who knows?

DEE: Who indeed? And now, S'ra Obelgerst-Levy, would you say that the discovery of this tomb of May-Cee overshadows in importance your unearthing of the great lintel and your translation of its message which has indicated how the Weans met their end?

LEVY: Indeed, I would.

DEE: We had hoped to broadcast from the site of the temple, but, of course, we can't be two places at once—

LEVY: No, we can't—but S'ra B'Han Bollek back home at the Museum already has my report on the temple's inscription. I'm sure he will be glad to give it. Frankly, I am unwilling to tear myself away from these ancient splendours—

DEE: I understand, S'ra Levy. So this is Kowly Dee at the tomb of May-Cee in n.yok, returning you to the Kenya Museum and Dinar Geb.

GEB: Thank you, Kowly Dee and S'ra Obelgerst-Levy, for an exciting remote. And now, S'ra B'Han Bollek, I wonder if you would be good enough to give us S'ra Obelgerst-Levy's report on the temple inscription at n.yok.

BOLLEK: Oh, that—yes, of course. I must confess I was

carried away with the magnitude of this newest find —weren't you, Haph-Bukong?

BUKONG: I will reserve my judgment until we see these artifacts from this tomb of May-Cee. I am a scientist, S'ra Bollek. Proof, S'ra. Facts and proof.

BOLLEK: Yes—well, now for the other great discovery of Obelgerst-Levy. We now have definite proof of how the Weans perished. For weeks Obelgerst-Levy has been excavating a great temple not far from where he has now discovered the tomb of May-Cee. On the lintel of this temple, he found this fragmentary glyph, which he translates as follows: "Snow, nor rain, nor gloom of night . . . their appointed rounds."

BUKONG: That's pretty obsure.

BOLLEK: Well, some of the hieroglyphs are missing.

BUKONG: "Their appointed rounds." What does that mean?

BOLLEK: You must realize, S'ra Bukong, that the "r" and the "w" are readily interchangeable in both the Hittite and the Hivite languages. You will admit this may be so in the ancient Wean language.

BUKONG: For the sake of argument.

BOLLEK: Very well, then. Instead of their "appointed rounds," the phrase may well mean their "pointed wounds," may it not?

BUKONG: It might, but what about the rest of it?

BOLLEK: Considering the difference we have already noted between the Brython and the Wean glyph, the word *nor* can be considered "north," and the word *gloom,* could be translated "doom"—and *night,* "fright—"

BUKONG: Then what have you got?

BOLLEK: The tragic story of the end of the Weans. "The north snow, the north rain, the north doom of fright their pointed wounds"—in other words, invaders from the north have annihilated the inhabitants.

BUKONG: But tell me this then, S'ra Bollek—how did they have time to inscribe this account of their annihilation on a great marble temple before they were annihilated?

BOLLEK: But that's the most obvious part of it. We know than n.yok was the most populous city in the Great West Continent—and why? Because at the end it was bursting with refugees. One by one, the great cities fell to the doom of fright from the north—Cha'ago—Loose Angles, or Ankles—Pound-Laundry. N.yok, an island bastion, was the last to fall. Knowing of the fate of others, the Weans built this temple, and inscribed upon its great lintel their fate, so that we who came later might understand what happened to them.

BUKONG: Sounds reasonable. But there is one more question.

BOLLEK: What is that?

BUKONG: We have read much in their scrolls of a city more important than any of those we have excavated.

BOLLEK: Miltown?

BUKONG: Yes, Miltown. What about Miltown?

BOLLEK: Our expeditions have searched and searched—but they have found no trace of a city called Miltown.

BUKONG: Strange.

BOLLEK: Yes. I daresay we will never know anything about the Weans, but we now know enough to evaluate them as a minor culture, with a rudimentary religion devoted to a god named Oscar, who was worshipped by rocking and rolling. They enjoyed their brief moment in history, established their hegemony in the land of We by killing off the aborigines. They built their empire, such as it was, by the sword, and when the sword rusted, they died by another's—even as Egypt and Babylon and Greece and Rome, leaving behind them curious city mounds, a splendid tomb, and no music. *Sic transit gloria Weans.*

GEB: Thank you, S'ra B'Han Bollek. And thanks also to the scientists, archeologists, commentators, and announcers that made possible this *Report on the Weans,* the greatest single event in this Astro-Physical Year of 7956 A. D. This is Dinar Geb, speaking to you from the Great Hall of the Ethical Museum of Antiquity at Kenya, returning you to the main studios of Radio Rhodesia.